A STRUCTURE OF PEACE:
THE ARAB-ISRAELI CONFLICT

A STRUCTURE OF PEACE:
THE ARAB-ISRAELI CONFLICT

John Stebbing

NEW CHERWELL PRESS · OXFORD

First published in Great Britain 1993
by New Cherwell Press
7 Mount Street, Oxford OX2 6DH
Copyright © 1993 John Stebbing

British Library Cataloguing in Publication Data
Stebbing, J.
A Structure of Peace: The Arab-Israeli Conflict
1. Middle East — International relations
I. Title

ISBN 0 9517695 2 9

Cover design by Jacques Welter

Printed in Malta by Interprint

CONTENTS

FOREWORD

By the Right Rev. George Appleton, CMG, MBE,
Anglican Archbishop in Jerusalem, 1969-1974

People in the Middle East and their friends in other parts of the world are now talking about making peace rather than making war. So these studies by John Stebbing are very timely, for his aim is to lift our sights to the great possibilities of coexistence and shared prosperity, if we will only fix our eyes on creating the future. His theme is that between us we have the wisdom, skill, technology and finance as well, if we only have the will.

He is well qualified to speak, for he has had experience of rural development and settlement in Africa, has worked with the Atomic Energy Authority, and for many years has studied the available reports and discussions concerned with the future development of the area, and given all who will read them carefully a vision of something to be created, a construction of peace, beginning with the rock and sand and scarcity of water of desert areas which could be turned into a homeland of cornfields and gardens.

His chapter on the research going on in the Negev, dealing with Solar Energy, Desert Architecture, Desert Agriculture, Irrigation and Water Cleansing and the Closed System whereby the water transpired by plants is recycled for further nourishment of the soil, is a thrilling one, not only for Israelis but for Palestinians also, and for nations further away, for, as he points out, one third of the world area is desert. It would be a tragedy if the only nations failing to benefit from this research and experiment should be Israel's neighbours in the Middle East.

Peace in the Middle East will release huge sums now spent on armaments to be used for development, for supplying water and fertiliser to convert sand into soil, for providing food for under-nourished people, for securing the abundant life which God wills everyone to have, for providing homelands for the refugees, Jews and Palestinians, where all can live in decent homes, with sufficient food, sound education, health services, care of the old and the young, all of which are now possible with modern methods, finance and technology.

I, like John Stebbing, am thrilled with the proposals of Dr. Ra'anan Weitz, Israel's outstanding expert in the problems of large-scale settlements in the semi-arid regions. These proposals provide a basis for discussion between Israelis, Palestinians and Arabs, and could well lead to the settlement of 100,000 Palestinian refugees in the West Bank and Gaza Strip, and later to similar projects in the Arab countries where Palestinian refugees are still waiting in camps, and still further to possible development in the Sinai desert.

There are many human and political problems to be tackled before this vision can be implemented — Israel's need for security and acceptance, the Palestinian sense of injustice, the refugees' hope of permanent homes and compensation, Jewish and Palestinian refugees alike, the tension in the minds of many Israeli soldiers serving in Lebanon, the widespread grief at the loss of every Israeli life, the love of Jerusalem and some agreed way of sharing in its life.

My experience convinces me that both sides to this fratricidal dispute are ready to negotiate but neither is ready to take the first step. Israelis and their supporters in the Jewish Diaspora feel that Israelis are vastly outnumbered by the Arabs: one hundred million to four million, and therefore the Arabs should make the first step: the Arabs say that Israel has been victorious in five wars and the victors should therefore take the initiative. An Egyptian diplomat has suggested that there should be a simultaneous declaration of intentions and mutual acceptance in Jerusalem,

Nablus, Cairo, Amman, Damascus, Beirut, Tunis, New York and Moscow. Wishful thinking? Certainly, but in the original sense of those two words!

I believe that Israelis will find that the Palestinians are their best friends in the Arab world. They want to take a full part in planning their own future; they want to choose their own spokesperson in negotiations and their own leader in founding whatever state is agreed. In accepting these rights Israelis will be living up to their own ideal of democracy.

The rewards of peace, the promise of prosperity are great: the setting to rest of parental anxiety for a happy future for their children, the filial desire for a secure and happy final period for their old folk similarly assured, a fulfilling of the prophetic vision of old men and women sitting happily in the streets of Jerusalem, no longer prematurely cut off by war, with the city full of children, playing safely and happily in its streets, and the weapons of war transformed into implements for growing food, and Micah, Isaiah and Zechariah rejoicing in the Eternal City of the Living God in the fulfilment of their vision of a world at peace.

24 October 1991

INTRODUCTION

Research awards from the Leverhulme Trust, and travel grants from the David Davies Memorial Institute of International Studies, and private sources, from 1972 onwards, made it possible for me to make a number of visits to the Middle East. In the course of these visits I was privileged to meet many Israelis and Arabs in responsible positions.

As a newcomer to the Middle East I had expected some difficulty. I had been a member of the Colonial Administrative Service from 1934 to 1960, followed by twelve years in the U.K. Atomic Energy Authority at Harwell and Culham Laboratory. I was not sure whether my Colonial Service background would commend me to the Arabs and Israelis I hoped to meet.

I had a most valuable meeting with the Agricultural Adviser to the Embassy of Israel. I explained my interest in the Kibbutz movement; in Palestinian resettlement problems as part of a future peace settlement; and, especially, in the rural economy of the Gaza Strip and the adjacent area of Sinai. I also wrote to the Director of the U.N. Relief & Works Agency (UNRWA) operations in Gaza of my hope to visit refugee camps in the Gaza Strip and later in the West Bank. The Embassy in London made arrangements for me to be shown the progressive agricultural work being done with the Palestinian farmers in the West Bank. The result of these preliminary contacts was that I received the greatest possible courtesy and help from the Israelis and the Arabs. The UNRWA staff also went out of their way to show me their work in the schools, hospitals and clinics and the widespread relief and welfare activities of the Agency. I received much help from St. Antony's College, Oxford; for four years as a Senior Associate

Member of the college and, since then, being allowed the use of its Centre for Middle East Studies.

Archbishop George Appleton, whom I was extremely fortunate to meet, gave me every kind of help and encouragement. The Archbishop has been devoted to the pursuit of peace and reconciliation in the Middle East for many years, stretching back to 1969-74 when he was the last Anglican Archbishop in Jerusalem. Nobody has a greater understanding of these many-sided problems.

In the preparation of this book I have used certain articles published in 'International Relations', the Journal of the David Davies Memorial Institute of International Studies, making essential and extensive amendments, mainly to avoid repetition but also to bring them up to date. I am indebted to the Institute for allowing this material to be published a second time, to the staff for their help on many occasions, and to Sandra Hutchinson for her most expert help over typing the manuscript. Finally, I am especially indebted to my wife for her support. I am deeply grateful for all this kindness.

John Stebbing,
Chichester, October 1992

THE ELEMENTS OF A VIABLE PALESTINIAN ADMINISTRATION

Very few people can visit the Middle East without feelings of wonder and hope: wonder, at Jerusalem, the great centre of three faiths, at the beauty of the ancient Middle Eastern cities and landscapes; and the hope that its many gifted peoples could perhaps find a new harmony to share all the hopes and possibilities of the region.

The political complexities of the Middle East are very great. They are a specialist diplomatic study forming an important, but not an exclusive part, of this more practical study which is concerned with the physical aspects, social responsibilities and functional needs of a Palestinian future in the West Bank and Gaza Strip. Ideally, the two approaches to peace should be followed simultaneously.

There are important comparisons to be made between the present situation in the West Bank and Gaza Strip, and that of certain British Colonial territories after the Second World War. This applies particularly to African territories which had large-scale European settlement involving extensive alienation of land, such as in Swaziland and Kenya.

After the war there was a period of increasingly intensive colonial development, widely involving the local populace, absorbing much of the energies of the community and overcoming many of their internal tensions during the approach to independence, including (where it might be possible) the recovery

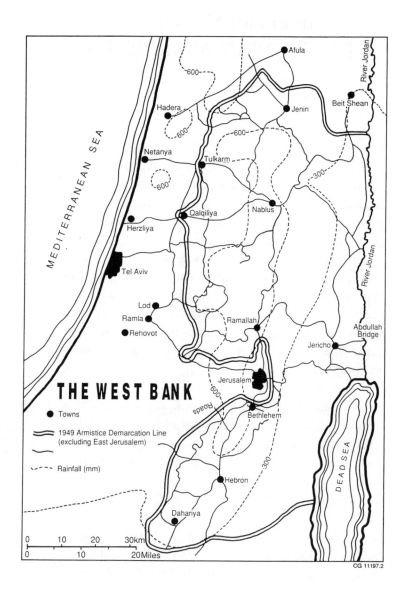

THE WEST BANK

● Towns

〰 1949 Armistice Demarcation Line
(excluding East Jerusalem)

╲‒‒‒ Rainfall (mm)

of areas of alienated land.

This colonial post-war experience could be very relevant in the aftermath of the Arab-Israeli conflict. If the present peace negotiations could reach an acceptable understanding of the basic conditions of peace in the Palestinian regions, this would provide the opportunity for the development and stabilisation of the wider Arab-Israeli areas.

My immediate impressions on visiting the Occupied Territories were of the great skill of the Israeli agriculturalists, and the Palestinians they had trained. They have been working throughout the West Bank, and to a lesser extent in the Gaza Strip. I have on many occasions admired the high quality of this work and the excellent relations existing between the Palestinian farmers and their Israeli and Palestinian supervisors. This is encouraging for the future. There is little doubt that, if the Arab-Israeli conflict could be brought to an end by negotiation, with sound agreements about land and water, in the West Bank and Gaza Strip, and with the progressive withdrawal of security forces from both areas, it would become possible by quite rapid stages to establish a viable and self-governing Palestinian administration.

Important parts of a possible administration do already exist in the organisation of the United Nations Relief and Works Agency for Palestinian Refugees in the Near East (UNRWA), which has been functioning since 1950 in all the refugee areas of the West Bank and Gaza Strip, as well as in Lebanon, Syria and Jordan. The Agency has been responsible for all primary and intermediate education; for all vocational training; and for health services for the most aged, destitute and needy of the refugee population. For years the Agency has had to call on UN member states to meet the cost of its operations, particularly the fine

3

educational services, which keep expanding. Until recent years this has been increasingly difficult.

Despite the earlier uncertainties of funds, and the widespread insurrection throughout the Occupied Territories starting in January 1988, the contribution of the UNRWA schools to the refugee problem has been one of real distinction in conditions of great difficulty and frequent danger. The refugee enrolment, in all areas, has risen from 43,000 in 1950 to the present total of 351,000. Out of the Agency's staff of 10,435 only about 100 are internationally recruited; the great majority of the remainder are qualified Palestinian teachers.

After nine years of elementary and preparatory education, pupils have the opportunity (until recently) to proceed to vocational and teacher training at Agency centres, to universities in the Occupied Territories, or in the Arab countries further afield. Unfortunately these institutions have been widely damaged during the recent disturbances in the Occupied Territories, and many have been closed for long periods.

Besides the economies in relief, welfare and medical services, UNRWA has had to cut down on building schools with the result that 75% of the 628 schools have to operate double shifts. Building has had to be confined to the replacement of only the most derelict schools and classrooms, and to avoiding the extreme difficulties of treble shifting.

The difficulties of double shifting, in which so many of the schools have two complete teaching staffs and two separate complements of pupils changing over at mid-day, are hard to describe. In spite of these handicaps the school results are exceptionally good and the percentage of eventual graduates is very high. Nobody who has visited these schools could fail to admire the resolution of the staff and pupils to overcome these difficulties. The provision of proper buildings and equipment would ensure that a future Palestinian administration has an excellent education service at these basic levels.

CONDITIONS IN THE WEST BANK

As the major region of any future Palestinian administration, the potential of this area for development must be decisive. The Israeli occupation has led to increasingly unfavourable pressures in maintaining law and order. There has also been the seizure of land and water supplies and the establishment of Israeli settlements. The West Bank Palestinian population has nevertheless made steady progress in agriculture and light industrial development. The well developed agriculture of the West Bank has been achieved under natural conditions; only 4% of cultivated land is irrigated, compared with 45% in the Gaza Strip. In recent years mechanisation has increased widely for ploughing, spreading fertiliser and crop spraying. New sprinkler and drip irrigation schemes have been started; the limited water supplies have been improved in some rural areas.

This progress has been achieved, under the guidance of Israeli agriculturalists, by an agricultural staff starting with 16 members and recently numbering over 5,000 workers (170 of them technicians) engaged in field service activities. These include extension, research and veterinary services. The technical staff are now predominantly graduate Palestinians, well suited to work among the conservative but efficient and very devoted West Bank farmers.

Field services receive support from soil, water and veterinary laboratories. Artificial insemination has been upgrading milk

5

cows. Improved agriculture and animal husbandry have stimulated higher yields, particularly of cereals, olives, almonds, vegetables and industrial crops, while at the same time the proportion of the population involved in agriculture has dropped from 60% to less than 40%.

WEST BANK AGRICULTURE
(Value I.S. Millions)

	1977/78	1978/79	1979/80	1980/81	1981/82
Wheat, barley, sesame, tobacco	20.6	34.4	82.3	181.5	246.6
Vegetables and potatoes	51.7	82.0	200.5	427.1	951.4
Melons and pumpkins	2.0	2.9	22.4	59.7	134.2
Olives	114.7	77.1	660.0	495.0	1900.0
Citrus	30.3	41.4	89.2	226.5	349.1
Other fruits	49.5	83.4	214.4	473.0	825.7
Total crops	268.8	321.2	1268.8	1862.8	4407.1
Meat	58.0	138.3	296.7	843.8	1471.2
Milk	28.9	64.8	124.7	317.8	572.7
Eggs	4.0	6.1	14.1	53.0	104.5
Miscellaneous	0.6	1.1	3.2	5.8	12.5
Total livestock & livestock products	91.5	210.3	438.7	1220.4	2160.9
Investments in forestry & new fruit plantations	2.6	5.1	8.9	24.0	58.0
Purchased inputs	53.5	95.7	226.8	611.0	1364.4
Income originating in agriculture	309.4	440.9	1489.6	2496.2	5261.6

(In reading this table one should bear in mind that price indices rose by more than 700% between 1976 and 1981.)

The steadily developing capability of West Bank agriculture is of central importance to the viability of a future Palestinian administration. In recent years West Bank agriculture has been subjected to increasing constraints applied by the military government; by the rapid increase in Israeli settlements; and by the expropriation of all unoccupied land as well as substantial developed areas. Removal of these restrictions will be essential to the resurgence of Palestinian agriculture, which will be an important factor in the achievement of peaceful conditions.

The progress in the small West Bank industries has been less rapid. Expansion is extremely difficult to assess as price indices rose by more than 700% between 1976 and 1981. There is a limited domestic market, undeveloped technology, and a lack of advanced expertise and investment capital. The West Bank also lacks natural resources so that most raw materials have to be imported. Local sources of power are relatively expensive. Industrial production is confined to food processing, beverages and tobacco, as well as textile goods and clothing. There are many small and medium-sized workshops in the West Bank and many small vehicle repair shops: 90% of all plants employ less than five workers. Many of these small concerns work on sub-contracts for Israeli industries.

Until the 1988 disturbances, transport was a thriving industry in both the West Bank and the Gaza Strip. It handled the labour force commuting to work in Israel; it moved the increasing agricultural output of both areas; it was essential for distributing building supplies throughout the whole of the area in support of the continuing building boom. The transport industry has absorbed many UNRWA/UNESCO trained automechanics, welders and body repairers coming from the Vocational Training Centres. More and more of these skilled technicians are available to start businesses in the towns, villages and refugee camps.

7

For a period after the 1967 War there was a reluctance to make long term investments in construction and fixed assets; home remittances from abroad ceased for a time; there were difficulties over imports of cement, wood and iron. But quarried stone and lime are abundant on the West Bank and stone is widely used. By 1972 private building had recovered to its pre-war level. It has since increased by over 230%, but must have been set back by recent events.

Employment of Palestinians in Israel increased steadily in recent years from 14,000 in 1970 to 43,000 in 1982: just over half were employed in construction; a little over 20% in industry and just under 10% in agriculture. Their wages formed a further important part of family remittances to the West Bank. But *migratory* labour commuting into Israel has been much reduced by the disturbances.

The education services in the West Bank normally operate 98 UNRWA schools with nearly 40,000 pupils and just over 1,300 teachers: half of them have to accept double shifts because funds have not been sufficient, over many years, to build the additional schools as they become necessary. These conditions did not prevent UNRWA from providing an excellent service until recently. However, 90 of the schools were effectively out of action in 1988 and 1989. Attempts were made by UNRWA to provide courses to be followed in the camps. But the Israeli authorities refused to allow the necessary material to be given to the children.

The health services in the West Bank have been under greatly increased strain. Regular immunisation programmes for school children had to stop, though less disruption was caused to the eight government general hospitals, the training units for nurses and midwives.

THE GAZA STRIP

The Gaza Strip is a distinct political entity. It was occupied by Egypt, but not incorporated, between 1948 and 1967. The administration was based on the Mandatory Laws and these remain in force as the main body of law today. There is a High Court, District, Juvenile and Magistrates Courts. The Civil, Educational, Medical and Agricultural Services were based on the population of the area at the time of the Mandate in 1948: this was about 80,000. There were 212,000 refugees in the Gaza Strip from the 1948 War: these people added to the original population, whose privations became worse than that of the refugees themselves — they gravely overcrowded the 362 sq km of the Strip. Relief was promptly arranged, and between 1950 and 1956 UNRWA made plans, with Egypt, to resettle 50,000 to 70,000 people in the Sinai east of the Suez Canal. This scheme was opposed by the Palestinians and fell through after the 1956 War. The population is now over half a million.

In the main, only seasonal work was available in the Strip, but a little employment resulted from relief activities, and some thousands of the younger generation were employed in Egypt. Otherwise the refugees were confined to the Strip and had no freedom of movement.

Nearly 254,000 refugees are still in camps and the total registered refugee population is about 469,400. This is an active community. Its vigour is clear from its results in agriculture, industry and construction. Many Gaza workers have migrated to the Gulf states and the countries of the West. After the 1967 war numbers of Palestinians began to travel daily into Israel; they reached 36,000 in 1982. In the next year 83 UNRWA staff members

9

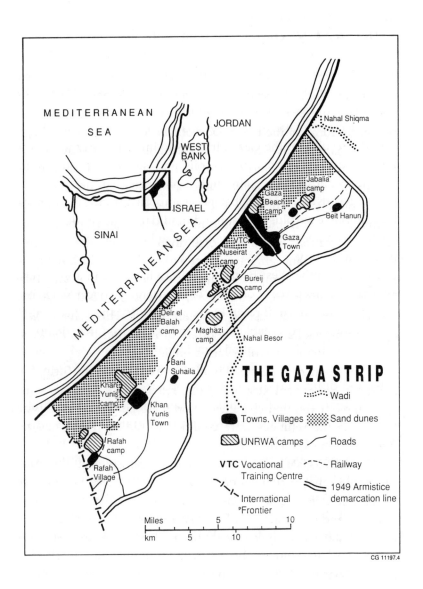

MEDITERRANEAN
SEA

JORDAN

Nahal Shiqma

WEST
BANK

ISRAEL

SINAI

MEDITERRANEAN SEA

Jabalia camp

Gaza Beach camp

Beit Hanun

VTC

Gaza Town

Nuseirat camp

Bureij camp

Deir el Balah camp

Maghazi camp

Nahal Besor

Bani Suhaila

Khan Yunis camp

Khan Yunis Town

Rafah camp

Rafah Village

THE GAZA STRIP

Wadi

Towns, Villages

Sand dunes

UNRWA camps

Roads

VTC Vocational Training Centre

Railway

International Frontier

1949 Armistice demarcation line

Miles   5   10

km   5   10

CG 11197.4

were arrested and detained, mostly for short periods.

Until recently agricultural output in the Gaza Strip has been subject to less fluctuation than in the West Bank, because 210,000 dunams[1], over half the total area, are cultivated, and 95,000 dunams are under irrigation. Seventy-five percent was devoted to citrus, which produced over half of the agricultural output.

Field crops make up a very small proportion of the whole, with the result that the Gaza Strip has to import nearly its whole consumption of grains, pulses, oils and sugar. The output of vegetables and potatoes, although it has increased, has not kept step with consumption: the balance is imported from Israel. There are exportable surpluses of almonds and dates; the production of meat, fish and eggs is generally increasing but imports from Israel are still necessary.

Here, as in the West Bank, agriculture has been in a vigorous condition. In the place of olives, it became largely concentrated on citrus production. Until recently, it appeared that these two major crops could ensure a stable and promising future for agriculture in a Palestinian administration combining the two areas. But there have been reports of reductions in the availability of irrigation water and difficulties over citrus exports.

Industrial production units remain small and in family ownership. Nevertheless the overall growth rate in recent years has been 4%. The 1982 labour force of the Gaza Strip totalled 82,000 persons; of these 44% were employed in Israel, a little over half in construction; there is normally a very large flow of workers commuting daily into Israel. The vigour and enterprise of the Palestinians is very evident throughout the whole area, particularly in small industrial projects. Recent disturbances have

---

[1] One dunam equals a quarter acre.

reduced the flow of migratory labour.

The concentration on education and vocational training which started in 1959 has resulted in an UNRWA/UNESCO school system which had an enrolment of over 351,000 children in 1988 and a teaching staff of 10,000 qualified Palestinian teachers and head teachers in 633 elementary and preparatory schools. A further 110,000 children were in government and secondary education.

For many years UNESCO and UNRWA, after consulting with Israel and Egyptian authorities, have organised the holding of the Egyptian school leaving certificate examination in the Gaza Strip; Egyptian examinations for university entrance and teacher training courses were also arranged. A similar flow of university students, financed by other Arab governments, left the West Bank to enter Arab universities.

Gaza education services follow the curricula of the Arab Republic of Egypt and the same year-by-year programme as in the West Bank. In 1988/89, 147 UNRWA schools had a population of 91,000. The standards maintained are normally very high and able students have good opportunities of acceptance by Egyptian universities. But between September 1988 and June 1989 two students were killed inside Agency schools, 376 injured by live rounds and rubber bullets, and 76 detained. Outside the schools 11 were killed, 3655 injured and 657 detained. The proposal to extend the school year was refused by the Israelis.

UNRWA organises two-year teacher training courses in four centres, two in Amman and two on the West Bank, at which enrolment in 1988/89 was 1,064. UNRWA maintained 453 scholarships for university study during the years 1988/89.

The vocational training arrangements are no less praiseworthy. Eight UNRWA training courses were operating in 1988/89; the

4,100 training places included courses (some mixed) in a wide range of metal and electrical building trades; commercial and paramedical courses, special vocational courses for girls. These two-year courses are equipping a steady flow of skilled workers, at present absorbed by the UNRWA services, by Israel and by the Arab world.

The Public Health Department of the military government and UNRWA together provide a comprehensive health care programme including preventative, curative and rehabilitation treatments. Out-patient curative medical care in UNRWA and UNRWA-subsidised clinics provides a full service. There are 600 hospital beds in seven hospitals. The special tuberculosis hospital is jointly operated by the Israeli authorities and the Agency. Nine ante-natal clinics, nine child health clinics, six rehydration-nutrition centres and a school health team serve the needs of the refugees. The Agency central laboratory is in Gaza. The recent disturbances placed these health services also under excessive stress.

Environmental sanitation, food hygiene and health education continue in support of wide-ranging immunisation programmes. Altogether, owing to the very fine health service here and in the West Bank, there has been no epidemic among the refugees, despite five serious wars and frequent unrest involving increasing military activity.

THE COMBINED ECONOMY OF THE WEST BANK AND THE GAZA STRIP

The effect of the combination of the two economies is to produce a much improved spread of resources and viability in a single economy. The combined gross national products of the separate regions in the six years following the 1967 War showed an average annual percentage rise of 18%. About 20% of the gross national product was (and in normal times still is) derived from migrant labour working in Israel and in the Arab world. The advances in the combined gross national product up to 1982 are summarised in the following table:

WEST BANK AND GAZA STRIP
Gross National Product (I.S. millions)
(*At 1968 prices*)

	1968	1976	1977	1978	1979	1980	1981	1982
West Bank	34.4	101.2	99.8	115.0	110.9	131.0	119.7	130.2
Gaza Strip and North Sinai	13.1	38.2	39.7	41.3	45.6	44.5	46.1	45.9
TOTAL	47.5	139.4	139.5	156.3	156.5	175.5	165.8	176.1

This table of the gross national product, at market prices, based on 1968 prices throughout, demonstrates the real growth over 14 years. *The combined economy of the two regions has increased nearly four-fold despite the difficult economic circumstances. This is very encouraging, particularly if peace negotiations can lead to the removal of present trade restrictions.*

14

POPULATION PRESSURES, LAND AND WATER PROBLEMS

Both the West Bank and Gaza regions have distinct population problems. The West Bank, with a 1972 population of 747,500 in an area of 5,505 sq km, has had to face the mounting pressure of the many new Israeli settlements, increasing the Jewish population from 800 in 1972 to 21,000 at the end of 1982 and far more than double that number today. The Jewish population is now just over 6%. If the projected total of 100,000 is reached the proportion of the total population is not likely to exceed 13%, unless there are massive deportations of Palestinians.

The danger in this situation is increased by the delicate population balance in the adjacent Northern District of Israel itself. Here the Arabs now comprise a little over 50% of the total population, and in a recent period of 18 years many more Jews have left the region than have gone to settle in it. The region is greatly affected by the unrest in Southern Lebanon.

Small population balances favourable to Israel have been recorded recently. But the Israeli policy of increasing settlements in the West Bank, at extremely heavy cost, where the prospect of achieving a settled community is so very unfavourable, has led to a reduction of funds for the development of new Israeli settlements within Israel itself. This stringency has been particularly evident in the Northern District of Israel; a clear Arab majority is likely in a short time and the age distribution makes it probable that this majority, and the obvious tensions in the area, will steadily increase.

There can be no doubt that a peaceful solution to this conflict will be impossible unless the Israeli West Bank settlements can be reduced.

The problems of water for agriculture are no easier than the problems of land. Besides the 4% of the West Bank under irrigation, much of the higher ground is in the area of moderate rainfall, 600mm or more a year. Large areas of the hillsides are terraced; these are ancient, stone built, and elegant. They follow the contour, conserve the rainfall and support six million olive trees, often interplanted with other crops. The terraces are too narrow for full mechanisation but much improvement in productivity has been achieved under Israeli guidance, in particular the hard pruning of olive trees, bringing a very rapid increase in olive production.

In the lower levels in the Jordan valley agriculture depends on 70 wells, and five groups of important springs yielding much water of fair to good purity for agriculture in the ideal hot-house conditions of the valley. The wells are said to yield 50 to 150 cubic metres per hour, and the five principal springs 1,900 cubic metres per hour. But the impact of Israeli settlements in this extremely productive area is very great. The percentage of water taken is not known but increasingly strict water rationing has been applied to Arab cultivators. Drilling for the Israeli settlements has lowered water tables; some drilling is so deep that long established Arab wells are badly affected. One very large oasis (Ouja) is reported to have dried up.

The Israeli extension service has assisted Palestinian farmers to adopt economical methods of irrigation. Wide ranges of crops are grown: tomatoes, eggplants, artichokes, celery, cotton and sugar. Citrus is the main orchard crop; lemons and oranges are of high quality, the latter in October well ahead of the rest of the Israeli crop which is marketed in January and February. High grade, heavy cropping bananas have also been developed; also many fine quality vegetables introduced by the research station in Jericho.

Communication between research and extension services is prompt and effective.

The underlying situation of land and water rights in the West Bank is well described in a recent official study by an expert Israeli group of professional researchers under the leadership of Meron Benvenisti, a former Deputy Mayor of Jerusalem. This unofficial research project has concentrated on the actual situation in the West Bank and Gaza Strip. In a preliminary report, the group observed that until 1979 the military government used the amended Jordanian expropriation law to acquire land for new public roads and approach roads to settlements. But 'since 1979 the Israeli government has seized practically any land needed for unlimited Jewish settlement in the West Bank.'

The Study Group summarised their conclusions as follows: 'The combination of land acquisition, closure of areas for military purposes and land use planning, roads and infrastructure development, has already ensured complete Israeli control over space in the West Bank.'

PALESTINIAN RESETTLEMENT IN THE WEST BANK AND GAZA/SINAI REGION

It is not possible to discuss the resettlement of Palestinian refugees without making certain assumptions, for instance the acceptance by Israel of a special highway linking the two Palestinian regions. Records are inadequate for assessing how many of the two million refugees have already been re-established in their host countries; how many could rejoin their families in Israel or the Gaza Strip; or how many have homes in the West Bank which are available for reoccupation. Substantial numbers will certainly hope to be resettled in the West Bank which must be the main reception area. Smaller numbers might be acceptable to some host countries. Of the camp population of 764,000 it should as a start be possible to resettle up to 250,000 in the West Bank (half in agriculture) and a small number in the Gaza/Sinai region; also to provide housing subsidies for the remainder to settle permanently in the improved, urbanised townships which could be developed from the present-day Gaza camps.

A new Palestinian authority may find that future planning falls into three parts: the preservation of UNRWA services for a transitional period of years; a full study of the needs of the new administration; and the formulation of a central government organisation.

The proposed refugee resettlement would require the construction of up to 200 new schools for Palestinian children. These, with the former Jordanian government schools, the existing secondary schools, the four vocational training centres and the three new universities, would form an effective and advanced educational system.

The medical services in the West Bank region need to be reviewed: the present 17 hospitals with 1,600 beds might need to be increased, particularly in the new resettlement areas. Out-patient services, especially in all branches of health and care and school services may well need expansion.

THE STIMULATION OF INDUSTRY

The present circumstances of the Palestinian people are not conducive to industrial progress. Nevertheless, spontaneous developments are to be seen throughout the West Bank and Gaza in every refugee camp. These range from garages; metal and wood workshops; tailors and dressmakers; bakers; small contractors; builders and retailers.

It is easy to underestimate the value of these small enterprises; in fact, they are the natural expressions of a vigorous, resilient, society living in restricted, often daunting circumstances. In this connection valuable observations have been made in the Report of the Independent Commission on International Development Issues on the nature of 'Informal Sector'. The report observes that similar societies derive their income:

from a myriad of small-scale activities: repairs, manufacturing construction, trade, catering and other services. With inadequate growth in job opportunities in the modern sector, the informal sector has grown rapidly. It is characterised by ease of entry, labour-intensive processes of production and distribution, traditional or easily acquired skills, low wages, and the use of local materials and simple tools and machinery. In many countries official policies have tended to neglect, or even to discriminate against, this sector.

In order to utilise the potential of the informal sector in assisting development, there is need to assist it through easier access to credit, training to upgrade skills, technical advice on product improvement, and the provision of better tools and infrastructural facilities. Encouraging of sub-contracting by larger firms and of purchasing by the public sector can provide new sources of demand. Joint purchases of inputs and assistance with marketing can enhance the bargaining strength of individual units and enable them to compete more effectively with larger domestic and foreign enterprises.

This constructive approach to individual progress is relevant to the situation in the camps. In spite of the extreme shortage of

19

funds, UNRWA has managed to give support for self-help schemes to enable refugees to pave pathways, construct drains, sewer-lines and water supplies in some camps. The Agency is also giving small scale encouragement of self-help in the form of building materials to improve the housing of refugees. The Agency reports that refugee communities are 'more than willing to participate in projects of this kind, but further financial support is needed to boost the programme.' Unfortunately, refugee housing has been widely damaged in the recent disturbances and a number of refugee homes deliberately destroyed.

With the help of governments, municipalities and local councils more basic community services have been provided; potable water; sanitary disposal of waste; stormwater drainage; the control of insect and rodent vectors of disease. The scale of this work needs to be extended. At the Amman New and Jabal Hussein camps about 2,700 shelters have been connected to the municipal sewerage system and the Jordan government is to provide this service to all refugees in the two camps. Indoor water taps are being provided on a self-help basis in all camps but this is a slow process.

Experience in British colonial dependencies during the years leading to independence has demonstrated the value of a working organisation of this kind. It could be simplifed to meet the specific needs of the Palestinians; it should be enlarged to meet the new responsibilities, such as law and order, justice, public works, industry, trade and communications. These responsibilities could be assumed in a reasonable time, possibly with some guidance from neighbouring Arab states. A large number of highly educated and experienced Palestinians employed in the Arab states and the countries of the West would doubtless be willing to work for the new administration.

THE ELEMENTS OF A VIABLE PALESTINIAN ADMINISTRATION

A great deal has already been done towards providing the basic needs of a Palestinian administration. There is no reason to doubt its viability, or the ability of the Palestinians to complete the remaining administrative structure.

2

PALESTINIAN ARAB SOCIETY IN THE WEST BANK AND GAZA STRIP

The impress of Ottoman power on the lives of the Arab people of Palestine has been profound and lasting. The main attribute of the Sultan's sovereignty was his right to every source of wealth in the Empire and his absolute authority to exploit it. It was the function of the ruling class to extend and preserve these resources and to cooperate in their exploitation, for the benefit of the Sultan and the state. For their part, the subject class had the obligation to produce wealth by agriculture, trade or industry and to pay part of the profits to their rulers in taxes.

Such a pattern of government need not have resulted in oppression and corruption if the provinces had been administered by persons of high calibre and the central government had been both vigilant and competent. Generally, it had been so up to the mid-16th century under the first rulers of the House of Osman. But the last rulers were 'incompetents, degenerates and misfits'[1]; as a result, standards of provincial government declined sharply in effectiveness and integrity.

The long decline of the Ottoman Empire extended over more than three centuries: its final disintegration followed the defeat of Turkey in the First World War. The decline in these standards is well illustrated by the deterioration in land registration. The Ottoman rule over the Arab lands is recorded in considerable detail up to the end of the 17th century. The cadastral surveys of

---

[1] B. Lewis: *The Emergence of Modern Turkey*, (London, 1968) pp 22-23

the provinces exist and each province has separate records beginning with the period of its acquisition or, in the case of the older provinces, beginning in the middle of the 15th century. The records start with 'a codification of the fiscal law and custom of the province, in the conquered provinces usually a codification of the pre-Ottoman usage with such modifications as the Sultan's government thought fit to introduce'.[2] These were guidelines to administrative usage and distinct from the Islamic law.

For Syria and Palestine there are detailed records of population, land tenure and revenue for the period mentioned. The tax registers give details of towns and villages by households and land holdings, whether gardens, orchards or under field crops. Revenues are listed in money and in kind. But the archives show that 'after 1600 the land surveys became less and less frequent and the resulting registers more and more slipshod':[3] the regular population censuses were abandoned. By the middle of the 17th century agriculture was failing; villages were being deserted all over the empire and the inhabitants moving into towns where there was insufficient industrial development to absorb them. Tax collection was handed over to tax farmers and agents who had no interest in rural society, in peasant welfare, or in the land, but only in the profitable abuses of tax collection. In the continuing neglect and inefficiency of the 17th and 18th centuries more and more peasants were forced into the hands of money-lenders and driven off the land. The central government no longer had any influence on rural society or agriculture, nor did the Turkish army make Palestine secure from rebellion and invasion.

---

[2] B. Lewis. Journal of the Royal Asiatic Society, October 1950, p 144ff.

[3] B. Lewis: *The Emergence of Modern Turkey*, pp 32-33.

In the 18th century a Bedouin sheikh rebelled against the Turks and set up an independent capital in Tiberias. The Turkish army eventually restored Turkish rule throughout Galilee, supported by a strong new provincial capital at Acre. Attempts were made during the 19th century to improve provincial administration. In 1838 committees were set up for agriculture, trade, industry and public works. Twenty years later a land code was introduced followed by commercial and maritime codes, all following French examples. Attempts were made to adopt the agricultural systems of Western Europe and some progress was made in abolishing tax farming. On the other hand, steps were taken to extend and confirm rights of land usage, possession and ownership with the result that the actual cultivators were often reduced in status to share croppers or hired labourers. However, the harmful effects of these latter measures were to some extent reduced by the inefficiency of their application.

Throughout the 19th century the Ottoman government continued to rely on local sheikhs for administration and tax collection; life was insecure and hard; settled agriculture in the plains was often impossible. Arab society met this external threat and the extremely spare conditions of living with a close-knit social organisation. This was based on the hamula, a kinship group made up of related, extended, families having a common ancestor. Each hamula lived in its own part of the village, dealt with internal disputes, was exogamous, held land jointly and worked it cooperatively. Each hamula was responsible for collecting its allocated share of the village tax, which it apportioned to every household. Hamula solidarity was essential to stability and protection. A typical village could comprise up to four hamulas, probably with a number of small unaffiliated groups, made up of refugees and people of lesser status. Despite rivalries in leadership, hamulas would cooperate to meet external threats and to maintain law and order within the village. Each village would act as a single political unit in relation to other villages.

> In the villages, all land, with a few exceptions, was state land and was held by the village community in a form of joint ownership called 'mucha'. The agricultural land was redistributed among the villagers periodically, usually every two years. There were different methods used for this redistribution, but the prevailing methods seem to have been, first to distribute the land, either permanently or periodically, among the hamulas of the village. Each hamula, then, distributed its shares among the heads of the extended families, each in proportion, either to his male dependents or to the number of beasts of burden in his possession.[4]

Hamula and village solidarity was essential to enable Arab society to secure its basic food supply; to meet the tax demands of the Ottoman government; and to face the constant challenge of Bedouin raids.

These nomad-peasant relationships had many fluctuating characteristics: there was the age-old antagonism between the followers of these two modes of life; there was at the same time the traditional claim of many settled peasants that they had Bedouin ancestors. Hamula wealth was still largely in livestock, housing was rudimentary and mobility not difficult. Professor Abner Cohen has observed that:

> Sometimes hamulas joined Bedouin tribes and became incorporated within their political organisation. It must be remembered that this was a society existing on the fringe of the desert. When security prevailed, masses of bedouin tended to settle permanently on the land, in the valleys and the

---

[4] Abner Cohen: *Arab Border Villages in Israel* (Manchester University Press, 1972) p 5.

plains, living in villages. When conditions in the villages were bad - when taxation was heavy and the pressure of bedouin was strong - the villagers tended to become nomadic. Nomadism had many advantages. Nomads paid no taxes, were not conscripted to the army, were armed (while the peasants were prohibited from keeping arms), could amass wealth in the form of livestock without being haunted by the unscrupulous tax collectors, and could even engage in occasional agriculture. They did not have to go far to the desert in order to be nomads, because large tracts of fertile land in the valleys and on the plains were available.[5]

The two-yearly basis of land allocation was designed to be fair; it followed the normal cycle of rotation of that time but led to land exploitation and erosion. This condition of land tenure continued into the Mandatory period, but communal holdings were beginning to be divided up, as private ownership began to replace ownership in common. With the decline of the Ottoman power, settlements, crops and livestock became more and more liable to Bedouin raids.

THE ARAB RURAL ECONOMY DURING THE BRITISH MANDATE

The Mandatory Government of Palestine became responsible for this outlying province of the defeated Ottoman Empire. It was exhausted by war. A civil administration took over from the military government in mid-1920 and the High Commissioner a year later described the condition of Palestine as follows:

The population had been depleted; the people of the towns were in severe distress; much cultivated land was left untilled; the stocks of cattle and horses

---

[5] Ibid., p 7.

had fallen to a low ebb; the woodlands, always scanty, had almost disappeared; orange groves had been ruined by lack of irrigation; commerce had long been at a standstill. A Military Administration was established to govern the country. For nearly two years it laboured, with great devotion, at its restoration. An administrative system, as efficient as the conditions allowed, was set up. The revenue authorised by the Turkish law was collected, and was spent on the needs of the country. A considerable sum, advanced by the Anglo-Egyptian Bank, was lent by the Government in small amounts to the agriculturalists, and enabled them to purchase stock and seed, and partly to restore their cultivation. Philanthropic agencies in other countries came to the relief of the most necessitous. Commerce began to revive. It was encouraged by the new railway connection with Egypt, established during the campaign for purposes of military transport. It was assisted also by the construction, with the same object, of a network of good roads. The country showed all the signs of gradually returning life. The methods of agriculture are, for the most part, primitive; the area of land now cultivated could yield a far greater product. There are in addition large cultivable areas that are left untilled. The summits and slopes of the hills are admirably suited to the growth of trees, but there are no forests. Miles of sand dunes that could be redeemed are untouched, a danger by the encroachment to the neighbouring village. The Jordan and the Yarmouk offer an abundance of water-power, but it is unused. Some industries — fishing and the culture and manufacture of tobacco are examples — have been killed by Turkish laws; none have been encouraged; the markets of Palestine and of the neighbouring countries are supplied almost wholly from Europe. The seaborne commerce, such as it is, is loaded and discharged in the open roadsteads of Jaffa and Haifa; there are no harbours.[6]

The Mandatory Government inherited the most formidable tasks. A complete framework of government had to be constructed, a judicial system and treasury established; an advisory council set up. There were no civilian hospitals, scarcely any schools; no agricultural, veterinary, forestry or fisheries services; no department of commerce and industry. All of these, and an effective

---

[6] An interim report of the Civil Administration of Palestine during the period 1 July 1920 to 30 June 1921. HMSO Cmd. 1499. 30 July 1921, pp 3-4.

public works department, a post office and police force had to be established.

By 1923, rural indebtedness and other pressures to sell land had resulted in 44% of the area being divided. An official enquiry in 1930 found many of these partitions were not final: partition could only be legally effected by the unanimous agreement of all shareholders and the acceptance of that agreement by the courts. This was extremely difficult to bring about. The alternative was a costly petition to the courts by an individual. As a result much unofficial partitioning took place, the majority of which was unsatisfactory from the agricultural point of view.

> As in all Oriental countries there is in Palestine a universal desire that each shareholder should have a share, however small, of each distinctive class of land. The result is that the plots of individuals are scattered here and there throughout the village, and are frequently either of ridiculous shape or too small for effective exploitation. Cases are known of fields being so divided that a share is 2,000 metres long and 4.5 metres broad.[7]

The report made clear that special measures were needed to speed up partitions which were essential to the achievement of a prosperous rural Arab economy. Land reform needed settled conditions and well qualified staff able to spend a long time in unravelling the difficulties which had developed over centuries. There were examples in which Arab groups were persuaded to redistribute the land so as to amalgamate the holdings, thus constituting economic blocks. But this took three times as long as ordinary partition. The settled conditions needed for such a careful rationalisation of land tenure were not available.

Meanwhile 85% of the Arab population still lived from

---

[7] Palestine. Report on Immigration, Land Settlement and Development. Sir John Hope Simpson, 1930, HMSO Cmd. 3686, pp 31-33.

agriculture. It was customary for every Arab head of a family, if he was a farmer, to provide 'muna', the basic needs of the household for 13 months. The young men of the family had a duty to assist in this and it was the duty of the father to provide the bridewealth for each son. With all the difficulties of undivided and inadequate land holdings life was on the borderline of starvation. In the latter 1920's a review was done of the economic conditions of agriculturalists, partly in order to commute the archaic tithe system followed by the Ottoman Empire.

The conclusions of the committee showed that the peasant population could not exist on a family holding of even 100 dunams (25 acres). The peasant farmers were 'hopelessly bankrupt'. The committee noted a progressive diminution in the areas of holdings (in the worst cases they were expressed in millionth parts); the selling of portions of holdings to pay off debts, government taxes and to obtain the wherewithal to live. At the same time the population was increasing and there was more competition for land, which sent up rentals to as much as 50% of the produce.

The committee considered the Arab peasant cultivator to be a competent agriculturalist, able to learn new methods, and to employ new capital if it could be made available. But, in the circumstances of the time, particularly the Jewish pressure to buy land and the general background of civil unrest, there was less and less chance to revive the Arab rural economy.[8]

Civil unrest started in the late 1920's and in the relatively quiet years of 1930-33 there was mounting tension about the sale of land to the Jews, particularly by absentee Arab landlords. By March 1925 the Jewish population was 108,000 and immigration,

---

[8] Ibid., pp 66-69.

which was 9,500 in 1932, rose to 30,000 in 1933 and nearly 62,000 in 1935. Serious disturbances broke out in 1936. From that time onwards Mandatory Palestine experienced continuous civil unrest until the outbreak of World War II. With the conversion of more land to private Arab ownership, class distinctions arose; larger Arab landowners became prosperous at the expense of more and more landless Arab peasants. At the same time a new horizontal stratification developed, cutting across the structure of the hamula, which lost much of its influence. The Arab nationalist movement was supported by the Islamic religious organisations; the mosques and Islamic funds were used to support the nationalist cause. The villages provided an ample supply of recruits for the irregular forces. Arab society was now devoted to the achievement of commonly accepted national objectives, if necessary, by force.[9]

The 1936 civil disturbances in Palestine were so serious that a Royal Commission was appointed in August of that year to ascertain the underlying causes, to discover whether the Arabs or Jews had legitimate grievances and, if so, to make recommendations for their removal. The Commission itself was delayed three months by widespread violence; it reported in mid-1937 that reconciliation was impossible and recommended the partition of Palestine between the Arab and Jewish communities.[10] A Partition Commission appointed in the following year reported, with two partition proposals, shortly before the outbreak of World War II. During the war, civil unrest was suspended in recognition of the greater external peril. After the war further attempts at partition led to the creation of the

---

[9] Abner Cohen, op.cit., pp 12-14.

[10] Palestine Royal Commission Report, July 1937, HMSO Cmd. 5479, pp 394-6.

State of Israel in 1948, followed immediately by the first of the five Arab-Israeli wars. The Palestinian Arab refugee problem is the product of this still unresolved conflict.

THE PALESTINIAN ARAB REFUGEE PROBLEM FOLLOWING THE WARS OF 1948/49, 1956, 1967 AND 1973

The United Nations Relief and Works Agency for Palestinian Refugees in the Near East (UNRWA) received a dual mandate from the United Nations under a resolution passed in December 1949, to provide relief based on need and to conduct relief measures to assist in the economic rehabilitation of the refugees. The Agency has worked continuously at this extremely difficult task, with great devotion; with generally meagre and, in recent years, insufficient international financial support. Details of the refugee movements are summarised in the sketch map on page 32.

Official UNRWA figures of refugees registered with the Agency on 30th June 1988 and their distribution:

East Jordan	899,811
West Bank	398,391
Gaza Strip	469,385
Lebanon	294,272
Syria	272,778
TOTAL	2,334,637

This situation resulted mainly from the first and third of the Arab-Israeli wars.

Non-refugee displaced persons[11] from the 1967 war were:

East Jordan	210,000
Syria	125,000

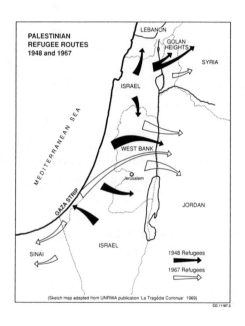

[11] Report of the Commissioner-General of the UN Relief and Works Agency for Palestine Refugees in the Near East, 1 July 1988 to 30 June 1989. General Assembly Official Records, Forty-fourth Session, Supplement No 13, (A/44/13), p 36.

THE WORK OF UNRWA AND UNESCO

UNRWA provides three services to the refugees: general education, vocational and teacher training; health services; relief. In recent years, shortages of funds have led to it confining relief to serious cases of deprivation and to some restriction of health services. The host governments supplement the services of UNRWA by providing, in some cases, upper secondary and university education, access to hospitals and other medical facilities, sites and water supplies. In the Syrian Arab Republic and in Jordan, the host governments bear the financial burden of caring for an estimated 300,000 persons displaced from territory occupied by Israel in 1967 who are not refugees registered with UNRWA.

The work of UNRWA, and more recently UNESCO, in promoting the economic rehabilitation of the refugees has fallen into three phases, officially described by the Agency as follows:

> During the period of 1950-55, much stress was laid upon large-scale development projects, directly associated with refugee settlement. These projects failed to achieve their purpose. In the ensuing period of 1955-59, UNRWA emphasised the smaller, practical self-help projects, along with basic relief. Since 1959 it has concentrated on expanding the much needed programme of vocational training for refugee youth, which the Agency had been conducting on a limited pilot basis since 1953. This programme is designed to develop the latent abilities of these young people to make them self-reliant, self-respecting and productive.[12]

---

[12] UNRWA Experience with Works Projects and Self-Support Programme: An Historical Summary (1950-1962). Information Paper No 5. UNRWA, Beirut, September 1962, p 1.

THE LARGE SCALE SETTLEMENT PROJECTS

The UN General Assembly placed great hopes on two ambitious settlement projects which they believed would provide for 200,000 people. These were irrigation in North-West Sinai to relieve the Gaza problem and a Yarmouk-Jordan valley scheme to assist the Jordanian refugees. Both schemes required extensive survey and major engineering works.

The Jordan valley scheme was to employ the waters of the Jordan and Yarmouk rivers to irrigate over 100,000 acres and settle up to 150,000 people[13]; nearly £0.5M was spent on survey work which extended into 1955.

The Sinai project was negotiated with the government of Egypt and it formed part of an Egyptian scheme to irrigate 370 square miles of land east of the Suez Canal for resettlement. The Agency was given the assurance that it might select a quarter of this for Gaza refugees. Irrigation water was planned to come from the Nile (less than 1% of its annual flow). It was calculated that this area would provide for 12,000 refugee families, or up to 70,000 individuals. The water was to be brought from the Nile by an enlarged Ismailia Canal and syphoned under the Suez Canal. The survey of this scheme and its technical planning also extended into 1955. This imaginative project would have provided a great deal of work for refugees, besides an extensive area for settlement: there was a good prospect that the sandy Sinai soil could be made as productive as that to the west of the Canal where citrus, mangoes, vegetables, cereals, groundnuts and dates grow well.

---

[13] Annual Report of the Director of the United Nations Relief and Works Agency for Palestinian Refugees in the Near East, 1 July 1953 to 30 June 1954. United Nations Official Records, 9th Session, Supplement No 17, (A/2717). New York, September 1954, pp 9-10.

Most unfortunately, the Sinai scheme was dropped after the 1956 Suez war and the Jordan valley project was confined to the Jordan section. Apart from the renewed hostilities there was opposition from the refugees themselves, who suspected that resettlement would prejudice their claims to eventual repatriation or compensation.

THE HEALTH SERVICES PROVIDED BY UNWRA AND THE MILITARY GOVERNMENT

The health services in the West Bank are governed by the Jordanian Public Health Act of 1965 supplemented by Israeli legislation. There are eight government hospitals in Hebron, Bethlehem (2), Ramallah, Jericho, Nablus, Tulkarm and Jenin. There are nearly 800 UNRWA subsidised beds in these hospitals with 70 beds administered jointly with the government of Israel, and throughout the Strip there are six maternity centres. In addition, throughout the West Bank and Gaza Strip there are curative outpatient services providing medical and dental treatment.

There is an expanded programme of inoculation against tuberculosis, diptheria, tetanus, whooping cough, poliomyelitis and measles. Environmental sanitation, food hygiene and health education continue in support of the wide-ranging immunisation programmes. This work is reviewed in Chapter 7.

PALESTINIAN ARAB SOCIETY TODAY IN THE WEST BANK AND GAZA STRIP

The traditional patterns in Palestinian society are changing fast. The close knit social organisation of the Ottoman period had begun to change to a more open society during the Mandatory period when local councils were beginning to take over some of the functions of local government. Towards the end of that time Arab national loyalties assumed more importance than local loyalties. But after the fighting in 1948/49, and the loss or departure of the entire Arab nationalist leadership, local society fell back on the defensive merits of the hamula.

The West Bank area was incorporated into Jordan and a degree of assimilation began to take place, though development was concentrated in East Jordan. The Gaza Strip was isolated; its people went through no process of assimilation. They are distinct, though no less a part of the Palestinian people. This distinctiveness may be the result of a whole generation under Egyptian administration. For a period, it seems that the hamula organisation became more rigid, with the change towards in-hamula marriages so that its members became more closely associated by a yet more extensive matrix of ties and relationships.

The changes after the 1967 war have been more rapid: increasing prosperity, advanced education, advancing agriculture; the developing equality of sexes, the sophistication of young people, radio and television, modern transport; migratory movements to work in Israel, the Arab states and the countries of the West. The effect of these influences on society over the last thirty years, and particularly in the last ten years, has been profound.

Education is seized upon by parents and children alike as an opportunity leading to well paid employment in the Arab world and beyond; as the most effective means of achieving an advanced society and a national future; and eventually bringing relief from the present difficult and overcrowded circumstances. The relationship between parents and schools is close and continuous; the achievement of equality between boys and girls has been a natural and welcome evolution.

The impact of radio and television has also been widespread. Radio is everywhere. The numbers of television aerials in Nablus and Hebron compare with the forests of aerials in east Jerusalem. Television is in the remotest villages and in the refugee camps, operated by dry batteries where there is no mains supply. Programmes are received from Jordan and Egypt as well as from Israel.

Agriculture is still fundamental to the future of these areas. It is progressing, particularly in the West Bank, where highly qualified Arab extension staff receive close support from the Israel Ministry of Agriculture and its resources in research. The agricultural output has increased rapidly in recent years even allowing for the high rate of inflation.

The agricultural industry has a promising future and this will continue for as long as there is expertise close to the farmer, with continuity of contact and guidance, and as long as research centres are closely in touch with the extension service. This service is predominantly Palestinian and highly qualified; liaison with research institutions in Israel is continuous and Palestinians are now beginning to take higher research degrees in agricultural subjects.

The expanding economy in the West Bank and Gaza Strip has overtaken the traditional concentration on subsistence agriculture.

'Muna' has been replaced by the purchase of food reserves by the head of the family. Bridewealth is earned by his sons, and the father of the bride will seek only to be assured that the marriage is an appropriate one and that the bridegroom can suitably provide for his daughter. Arranged marriages no longer happen; marriages take place only after full agreement between the prospective partners; parents can offer advice but they no longer have the last word.

Youth organisations of a constructive character have begun to appear in the camps. These spring from a desire to build up their society and their country; young educated men are playing an active part in camp committees. Prosperity among the young people has also introduced them to drink and tobacco. Young men (with help over costs from UNRWA) have developed Youth Activities Centres for sport and recreation in the camps. In one camp young women graduates collected IL. 15,000 (nearly £1,000) for a Women's Activities Centre. The family attitude to hospitals and clinics has also changed; 25 years ago mothers had to be persuaded to bring children for treatment, now they attend without question.

When the West Bank and Gaza Strip economies were brought into contact with the economy of Israel, Palestinian Arab society gradually became more open. Today, in response to all the influences described, there seem to be two closely inter-related levels in Palestinian society. The hamula organisation at its base is still very important. It continues to be the kinship group, concerned with preserving harmony between its constituent extended families; dealing with external as well as internal disputes; concerned with the continuity of the group. But the hamula influence does not pervade every social occasion as in the past. Hamulas today appear to divide society vertically, providing a stable traditional base above which there is developing a country-wide class of highly educated professional people, both women and men. This is horizontal in character, complementing the traditional organisation and to some extent interwoven with it. There appears to be no conflict between these two expressions of society; indeed the structure of society is, as in the Ottoman period, a reflection of the circumstances of the time. Society is firmly rooted at its base and the horizontal character of the upper stratum provides a unifying influence. Mukhtars and other traditional leaders are to be found among the highly qualified graduates holding responsible posts. Sons and daughters from almost every home are joining the professional classes. These classes have formed modern societies which extend far beyond the local village; some of these are devoted to social betterment, such as the Red Crescent, which has done valuable work in the Gaza Strip, where it plans to build a new hospital.

The opening up of a Palestinian society, more evident in the West Bank than in the Gaza Strip, has had its influence on the traditional authorities. The office of Mukhtar is no longer accorded almost unquestioning respect; much depends on the character of the holder in the present circumstances. This is soon apparent to his people. Some holders of this office refused to continue under the military administration; of the rest some gained respect for their conduct, others did not. The seal of Mukhtar, formerly accepted on documents throughout the Arab world is now issued by the Government of Israel and is not accepted outside Israel and the occupied area; its use is restricted to formal purposes such as the registration of births and deaths, marriages and divorces, and travel permits.

The authority of the Mukhtar has been affected by the increase in education. Before 1948 a village of 3,000 people might have four or five men with secondary education. Now there would be at least 15 to 20 doctors, lawyers and graduates of every kind. Many Mukhtars and elders have three or four graduates in their families.

In the West Bank, prosperity has brought the improvements in housing already mentioned and the wider dispersal of family activities. Television, radio and modern housing have lessened the importance of the diwan as a central meeting place. But the hamula meets when needed. In cases of quarrels and violence it will take steps to separate the parties for a cooling period. In a dispute within the hamula, the aggrieved party would today try to settle the matter by discussion, particularly if he is a highly educated person; but failing this he would go to the head of the hamula who would send out to call members to attend a meeting. The hamula authority still extends to all of its members although today they might be dispersed into different refugee camps or far beyond the borders of the West Bank and Gaza Strip. The hamula exists to preserve these ties, to solve problems and maintain peace. Even in the dispersed conditions of today, there is no report of a member permanently dissociating himself from these rights and obligations. Great importance is attached to education, but when trouble comes members will not act alone. The head of the hamula will call a meeting; free discussion will follow and the wisest proposal will be adopted, no matter who may have put it forward. The goal is to achieve lasting peace and not to solve problems by creating others.

The hamula is particularly concerned with matters such as killing, rape, and major thefts. Only if the hamula cannot settle the matter will recourse be had to the courts. In a killing a reconciliation could never be arranged independently of customary procedures; the whole hamula membership will contribute equally to the diya, or blood money: the offending member will only pay one share.

The procedures for inter-hamula disputes are far more formalised. First, the heads of the two hamulas will arrange a truce, 'while the iron is hot', during which no member of the complaining hamula may meet any member of the other hamula. This truce will be extended if necessary until a reconciliation is achieved. During the truce period there is the risk of reprisals: a friend of the victim, as far away as Damascus or Amman, could kill any member of the offending hamula whom he might happen to meet, in the presence of independent notables; the committee will then reply. The party causing the injury will discreetly place the money under a mattress in the meeting place; often this will finally be returned if the other party comes to regard the injury as a matter of providence. If the two hamulas fail to reach an agreed decision, there are procedures for appointing an arbitrator acceptable to both sides, whose decision will be final. The agreed terms of the reconciliation will in any case be fully written out and sent to the court.

Besides these important hamula functions devoted to maintaining peace and equilibrium in Palestinian society, the hamula performs valuable social functions by collecting funds from wage-earners (and from graduates working in Arab countries, the USA or United Kingdom), usually 5%, to pay for university education fees of other hamula members. In due course these loans are repaid by the new graduates so that the schemes operate as revolving funds, issuing more loans as earlier loans are refunded.

The hamula organisation has proved capable of change and modernisation; it is as strong in the towns as in the villages. In Gaza, the hamula organisation was described as the expression of the Palestinian entity at every political level: there is the 'hamula' of the village; of the Gaza Strip; the 'hamula' of the whole Palestinian people; and, indeed, the 'hamula' of the Arab world.

Palestinian society is functionally thriving in spite of the disintegrating influences of the last 40 years. It is in a constant state of progressive change; it is a coherent and vigorous society well able to take a balanced view of the political situation; and the Palestinian people are well equipped to create a separate self-governing administration which is compatible with both Israel and Jordan. Moderate professional elements in the West Bank and Gaza regions well appreciate the need to maintain close and cooperative links, and open borders with both Jordan and Israel. Formalised association with Jordan is a real possibility; a wider Benelux type of association of the three regions is a realistic objective.

Speaking in London at the end of 1971, when he was Minister for Foreign Affairs of Israel, Mr. Abba Eban said:

> A peace resting only on a document would be a fragile and transient thing. The guarantee of peace in Europe is not the documents, with due respect to them, but that old rivalries between States have been put into the past, and thousands and millions of Frenchmen, Dutchmen, Germans - from countries where previously there were four separate states at war - are now intermingled so intimately, that if they wanted to make war they would be unable to separate themselves into the hostile confrontation necessary to war. So in addition to our documents we must see that we can bring in this mutual flow of Jordanians, Lebanese, and others, joining together with us.

There could be no more helpful approach to an enduring solution of the Arab-Israeli conflict.

3

JEWISH RURAL SETTLEMENT IN ISRAEL

From the earliest years of the State of Israel, David Ben-Gurion, the first Prime Minister, stressed that the Negev was the proper direction for Israel's expansion of settlement. The Israelis have developed new opportunities in the Negev desert, where they have done some of the most brilliant desert research, with the aim of new and imaginative human settlement.

The Palestinians, for their part, also need the fullest possible area of the West Bank and Gaza Strip. As already explained, they might be assisted by Egypt granting the right of settlement in a small area of the Sinai desert close to the Gaza Strip. This would be a voluntary repetition of the major offer of Palestinian resettlement in the area to the east of the Suez Canal, made by Egypt in 1957.

To the Israelis and Arabs alike, the security and progress of their agriculture is a vital component in any enduring peace. Both peoples require intensive rural settlement in secure conditions. Besides this, essential defensive understandings have to be negotiated covering the whole of the West Bank and Gaza Strip. Upon the resolution of these conflicting claims the possibility of Arab-Israeli peace depends. Painful compromises will be inevitable on both sides. If these are possible, a new period of fruitful cooperation could follow. Most unfortunately, numbers of Jewish immigrants from the Soviet Union have been settled in the West Bank on the assurance that this area forms a part of Israel.

Advanced agriculture in Israel is older than most of the Old Testament, which speaks of produce of many kinds. In about 1000 B.C. Abigail took David two hundred loaves, two bottles of wine, six sheep ready dressed, five measures of parched corn, a hundred clusters of raisins and two hundred cakes of figs.[1] The Dead Sea Scrolls include a quotation of a letter from a cultivator in the Jordan valley, written in about 100 A.D., asking a friend to send him myrtles and willows, in exchange for the palm and citrons that he was sending on two donkeys.[2]

In the Negev 1400 years ago the Nabatean people gave up skilful desert irrigation, not because it failed, but because the trade routes bringing Indian and Arab spices, perfumes and Chinese silks across the Negev desert were superseded. And so they abandoned an ancient and carefully developed system to the nomadic Bedouin tribes. Happily, the Bedouin had no use for agriculture beyond growing an occasional grain crop and then leaving the area for years, or for ever. By this fortunate turn of events the deserted Nabatean lands and irrigation works remained largely undisturbed until today. They now provide conclusive evidence that a settled and civilised standard of life was achieved in the Negev desert by using the scarce rainfall draining down from the hillsides to make good the erratic and generally inadequate rain falling directly on to the cultivated areas. The Nabatean people had observed that the loess soil in the area formed an almost impenetrable surface after a light shower and as a result the hillsides absorbed very little rain; in carefully chosen areas rainwater was collected into run-off channels and led into a succession of terraced fields under the control of well-

---

[1] Samuel 25, verse 18.

[2] The Dead Sea Scrolls in Jerusalem.

designed shutters. This system made it possible to collect the rainfall from an area 20-30 times greater than the cultivated area and so produce the effect of enhanced, and adequate, rains.

The Nabatean farms at Avdat and Shivta, 30 miles south of Beersheba, were brought back into productive use 20 years ago and have contributed very greatly to the modern study of desert agriculture.[3]

When the Romans drove the Jews out of Palestine, they drove out a people who were very skilled agriculturalists and pastoralists. But since they did not have access to land in the countries to which they went, for 19 centuries they were mainly urban dwellers. Throughout this long interval there were small but influential Jewish communities in Palestine but there were no concerted moves to return, until the late 19th century when the Zionist movement began to assume international significance. With the consent of the Turkish authorities a new Jewish suburb of Jerusalem was founded in 1860; an agricultural school was started near Yafo in 1870 and in 1878 came the development of Petah Tikva, 'the mother of settlements', by immigrants from Hungary and Russia. By 1900 there were 22 villages, and citrus, olive and eucalyptus plantations were started, using paid labour. By 1914 there were 90,000 Jews in Palestine, including 43 agricultural settlements mainly promoted by Baron Edmond de Rothschild. There was then a tendency to concentrate on cash crops in preference to subsistence farming.

In 1909 a 'kvutz' or group settlement was started in Degania at the southern point of the Sea of Galilee. This was a socialistic experiment in collective living; it became the first kibbutz. The principles adopted at Degania were: purely collective production

---

[3] Michael Evenari and others: *The Negev. The Challenge of a Desert* (Harvard University Press, 1971).

by the whole community without the use of hired labour; communal living; collective disposal of produce for the benefit of the settlement as a whole. Members handled no money (except for small sums for use as pocket money) and private ownership was confined to essential personal possessions. The settlement has since grown and divided into two kibbutzim which provide a fine example of what a kibbutz can become. In 1921, a Degania group with differing ideas moved away to form a new type of settlement; this started as a cooperative small-holders' village in the valley of Jezreel and became the pioneer moshav. The new settlement was run on the basis of cooperative production, cooperative local government and cooperative distribution; the equal sharing of land with a guaranteed minimum living standard; with consumption and living arrangements on a family basis.

This form of settlement is now met with in two forms: the collective moshav which, like the kibbutz, has collective methods of production, though, unlike the kibbutz, individual consumption is on a family basis; and the cooperative moshav, now by far the most widespread, which has no collective activities, except perhaps for the initial clearance of the ground and during the harvest — a multi-purpose cooperative embracing all economic activities.

The political contribution of the kibbutz, and later the moshav settlements, has been of the greatest importance to Israel. Joseph Ben-David[4] describes the impetus which led to this development:

> One of the central ideas of the Zionist Movement was that only through the creation of a broad stratum of agricultural population could the Jews strike

---

[4] Arid Zone Research XXIII, Agricultural Planning and Village Community in Israel. Edited by Joseph Ben-David. UNESCO, 1964, p 47.

real roots in their homeland. Its members believed in physiocratic theories extolling primary production as the chief source of the wealth of nations, and they hoped that widely dispersed agricultural settlements would determine the Jewish character of the land. Jews in Europe and the Middle East rarely owned land and were concentrated in business and other middle-class occupations. In order to become an independent nation they had to perform all work necessary to a society. Agriculture, the most difficult and to Jews the most alien kind of manual work (though it had been the typical occupation of ancient Jews in their own country) became the symbol of national transformation. As a result the Zionist movement embarked on a policy of buying up barren land with a view to reclaiming it for purposes of agricultural settlement.

Though limited in numbers, the first pioneers from Russia and East and Central Europe attracted widespread interest. Agricultural training was arranged before groups left for Palestine; nearly 5,000 immigrants, registered as agricultural workers, entered the country between 1919 and 1923. Many had received special training.[5]

The Balfour Declaration of 1917 committed the United Kingdom to support the establishment of a Jewish National Home in Palestine after World War I, provided that nothing should be done which might prejudice the civil and religious rights of existing non-Jewish communities in Palestine. This undertaking the Arabs claimed to be inconsistent with other wartime assurances given by representatives of Great Britain that the Arabs would be given an area of independence when peace came. However, the Balfour Declaration was incorporated into the terms of the League of Nations Mandate; Great Britain became the mandatory power and separated Transjordan as a purely Arab state, excluded from the Balfour Declaration. Neither Arab nor

---

[5] Ibid., p 48.

Jewish nationalism was satisfied. Jewish immigration became more rapid and in 1933 it exceeded the birth rate of the Arab community.

The anti-Jewish measures of Nazi Germany in the later 1930's led to further increased immigration, and increasing Arab opposition; to attempts by the British to restrict Jewish immigration which, in turn, led to yet greater tension approaching civil war. The Jews however supported the British in the 1939-45 war; at the same time they were looking ahead to the situation which had to be faced when peace returned and a still greater flow of immigrants had to be settled. They established three kibbutzim in the Negev in 1943, Revivim, Gevulot and Beit Eshel, to discover whether large scale settlement would be possible in this northern part of the Negev desert. These settlements succeeded; a further nine were founded in 1946 and seven more in 1947. The continuing restrictions in immigration which followed World War II did not stem the flow of immigrants: by 1948 there was a total of 138 kibbutzim of which 21 were in the Negev. The 21 Negev settlements had an important strategic as well as an agricultural role. They played a large, possibly decisive, part at the end of the Mandate by delaying the advance of the Arab armies in 1948. They very soon developed a scientific approach to desert agriculture.

It has been suggested that the character of the kibbutz underwent a change after the creation of the State of Israel. Up to that time these settlements appealed to dedicated idealists who were prepared to apply their capacities in a new enterprise which matched their idealism. The organisations which promoted and financed the settlements were representative of the Jewish political (and religious) spectrum and at the time of independence the settlement movement provided a large proportion of the new political, civil, and defence leaders and the managers. Naturally, the functions of running the state, and defending it, attracted the services of many leaders in the settlement movement; there has been no decline in the special appeal of the kibbutz, or the moshav, though there is evidence that some of the rigours of kibbutz life are being modified. For instance, the separation of children is less strictly applied by the new generation of parents. Until recent years the young people often preferred the challenge of breaking new ground to settling in the kibbutzim of their birth, forming into groups at their high schools to create new settlements in the Sinai desert.

There has been evidence of rather high wastage in membership during the formative stages of recent kibbutzim; this problem of stability has never been absent from the establishment of settlements. It arises partly from the lack of the intensive preparation which was available to the first immigrant pioneers in the 1920's and early 1930's; also because settlers drawn from Israeli homes have a ready welcome back and the country is still in a state of rapid evolution offering wider fields of opportunity.

Kibbutzim still attract elitist elements dedicated to a communal society which depends on the close integration of each member into a wide range of activities; integration so far-reaching that the loss of a member, and still more a family, is felt by the whole community. Direct replacement is impossible, and intricate social adjustments have to be made. Membership still rests upon hard work which is disproportionate to personal reward; in which satisfaction is found in the quality of work and the prosperity it brings to the community. Men and women still live permanently without police, courts or prisons, or any form of compulsion. 'Everything is based on consensus, the social contract and domestic procedures whose resolutions are accepted by all despite the powers that be.'[6] For over 30 years industry has been progressively introduced into settlements to absorb manpower surplus to the needs of agriculture. By the end of 1980, agriculture no longer provided the greater part of kibbutzim prosperity. Kibbutzim in 1980 had 300 factories employing 12,000 persons (two-thirds of them kibbutz members) producing 5.6% of Israel's total industrial exports.[7]

REGIONAL DEVELOPMENT

In the early 1950's a new settlement problem arose with the arrival of large numbers of Jews from the Arab countries of North Africa, the Middle East and the Far East. It soon became apparent that people from these strongly traditionalist societies did not adapt as readily as the Jews of European origin to the standard patterns of settlement, also the flow of immigrants was so rapid that they had to be transferred direct from the ship to their settlements. As the new settlers had very little experience of agriculture, arrangements were made to assist each moshav family with expert supervision from the start. As families gained competence, this supervision was withdrawn until they assumed full responsibility for their holdings.

A new approach was made to the social, economic and security problems involved.[8] The key elements of this second phase in the development of rural settlement methods were:

---

[6] The Kibbutz 1910-1980, Dov Bar-Nir. New Outlook, Middle East Monthly, Nov/Dec. 1980, p 22.

[7] Kidma:Israel Journal of Development. No 21/1980 (Vol 6, No 1), p 34.

[8] The Lakhish Region, p 4.

1. the evolution of a composite rural structure for a whole region;

2. the creation of a pattern of local regional government and economic services instead of relying on the services of the more remote central government;

3. the development of a regional consciousness linking the settlements, through intermediate rural centres, to regional towns; to absorb as many immigrants as possible into wider Israeli society;

4. the creation of a new type of farm unit known as the Field Crop Farm to help overcome international trade imbalances.

The work was planned by the Settlement Department and put into effect through a Regional Director who was given a budget, a regional staff capable of developing the whole complex of settlements with regional services, and a major new town to become a regional centre.

The Lakhish regional scheme covers an area of 1,100,000 dunams in the area between the West Bank and Gaza Strip. It absorbed 53 settlements established before 1954 and added 17 new settlements, mainly in the area of Lakhish itself, and included the new urban centre of Kiryat Gat. It has been successful in absorbing large numbers of immigrants in productive settlements away from the centres of population; in increasing industrial crop production and helping the balance of payments. The region's three-tier structure has done much to stabilise the community as a whole. The individual settlements have, generally, been made homogeneous because past experience has shown that the extra solidarity that this provides is very important in achieving a well rooted community. Groups of settlements have been planned round the larger rural centres which, typically, have a primary school, a clinic, a library and cultural centre, a cooperative store and a bank. It is the intention and hope that the mixing of children at these schools, combined with the use by adults of the common rural services will gradually harmonise the peoples of differing origins from the various settlements. The large agricultural towns of Kiryat Gat and Sederot provide a further stabilising influence with their major facilities such as sugar refineries, cotton ginneries and regional banks, along with provision of entertainment, sports and shopping facilities at no great distance from any settlement.

This new rural organisation attracted the notice of the developing countries in Africa, Asia and South America, many of which have sought Israeli technical assistance in meeting their own problems of rural settlement. This, in turn, contributed to the Israeli decision to set up the Settlement Study Centre at Rehovot to keep the subject under continuing review. One of the tasks of the Centre has been to carry out an inter-disciplinary background study of the Lakhish region after 15 years of experience.

The overall growth of the Jewish population in rural settlements from 1948 to 1978 was 50,000 throughout the 53 kibbutzim of that time and 113,000 in 280 moshavim settlements. By contrast the Jewish urban population rose from just over half a million to nearly three million people.

These changes in the character of settlement in Israel are reflected in the figures of Jewish immigration: in 1978 a total of 20,757[9] immigrants were absorbed. This total included 11,222

---

[9] Ibid., p 143.

persons who had defined occupations abroad. Of these, 5,597 were engaged in liberal professions; 5,043 were managers and clerical staff engaged in transport, communications, building, mining, industry, commerce and services. Only 50 were agricultural workers — a very different situation from that prevailing in the years following the First World War. The population in kibbutzim is now only a little over 3% of the total Jewish population but it is still extremely influential.

INTEGRATED RURAL DEVELOPMENT

The wide international interest in the Lakhish regional development led to the Settlement Study Centre being consulted for regional schemes in Crete, Northern Burma, Venezuela and north-east Brazil. At the same time the Centre at Rehovot was working on a more comprehensive philosophy of regional settlement based on the continuous observation of the Lakhish region: the conclusions reached have been published.[10]

This remarkable study has led to a statement of the principles of rural development which will have the widest application. In describing the Rehovot approach it states that 'any plan with the ambition of changing the existing situation in any rural area in the Third World must be carried out by professionals who can cope simultaneously with the economic, social, physical and organisational aspects.'[11] As part of the economic process it

---

[10] Professor Ra'anan Weitz: *Integrated Rural Development: The Rehovot Approach* (Settlement Study Centre, Rehovot, Israel, 1979).

[11] Ibid., p 28.

stresses the need for simultaneous planning of the three sectors of the economy: agriculture, industry and services. In a recent study, by Professor Ra'anan Weitz and colleagues for the World Employment Programme of the International Labour Office, this principle was followed. The study aimed at establishing the employment and income generated by new settlement projects in the rural sections of developing countries. Sixty-three projects in 30 countries were surveyed.

This international recognition of the value of the Rehovot approach to integrated rural development in its application to Third World countries is a measure of the achievement by Israel in this sphere. Under the Rehovot procedure a composite plan has to be approached first by planning the three sectors separately.

The agricultural sector is based on the choice of farm type, its combined productive factors, its crop and animal husbandry patterns. The aim is to achieve balanced overall production without specialisation, determined by the economic stage of the country concerned, the local ecology, the degree of technological advance and the level of proficiency of local farmers.

It is recognised that these factors are not static. Planning must take account of tendencies towards change in technology, in farming capability and in the demand for the products of agriculture. The farm-type is designed to allow for change and modification. The Rehovot experts take the greatest care to develop an agricultural economy which is appropriate to the local situation.

Much stress is laid upon the need to ensure that the farm unit fully absorbs the family effort, using sophisticated methods to achieve high volume production. Over-mechanisation is not recommended as it can easily produce excessive unemployment. Also to be avoided is too great a concentration on export crops, as this tends to monopolize scarce capital and to lead to disguised unemployment by requiring temporary hired labour at times of peak activity; export crops should be cultivated collectively and form part of a village cooperative.

The sector plan for agriculture should take account of market research and the basic constraints of land and water potentials, as well as available manpower and finance; investigations should cover export possibilities of agricultural crops as well as domestic demands.

The Industrial Sector plan has to be based on extensive data concerning existing industries and similar industries outside the region, also the possibilities of new technology. The plan should embrace detailed elements covering manufacturing, handicrafts, construction, transport and communications, public utilities and the supporting infra-structure.

The Services Sector is made up of public services such as education, health, welfare, police, post-office; municipal and extension services such as trade, commerce and banking.

Next, the three sector plans have to be integrated into a comprehensive economic regional plan. At this stage adjustments in sector plans become necessary. It has to be recognised that no predetermined plan can allow for all the social, economic and physical problems which arise when the plan is set in motion. Discretion must be exercised in meeting the difficulties which are inherent in the process of development.

The experience of the Rehovot School over 30 years shows that Integrated Rural Development is an effective tool for solving the basic problems in the rural areas of the Third World. The regional importance of the school is very great. It has the most up-to-date professional experience of this area of Israel and the Occupied Territories at the time when effective resettlement will have an extremely important contribution to make in the evolution of peace in the Middle East.

4

ISRAEL'S SCIENTIFIC APPROACH TO SETTLEMENT IN THE NEGEV DESERT

Research being done by two institutes of the Ben-Gurion University of the Negev in Beersheba has brought Israel to the threshold of creating new forms of desert settlement in the Negev. These studies are comprehensive in scope and could be of extreme importance to every arid region; for Israel this research will provide wide areas for carefully controlled settlement — a most valuable contribution to peace.

The Applied Research Institute of the University has a range of projects with a direct application in both industry and agriculture; the objective is the prompt introduction of research results into the market-place. It is concentrating on the agricultural development of the Negev, studying the possibilities of exploiting its valuable natural resources: the vast uncultivated areas; the available geothermal heat; the abundant solar radiation; and the very large groundwater reserves. New agricultural technologies and new strains of desert crops are being developed to increase the economic potential of Israel; work is being done on the improvement and the improved management of drought-resistant and salt-resistant agricultural plants.

Research into the use of brackish water has already provided the economic basis for the establishment of three agricultural settlements in the Negev Desert.[1] Besides the introduction of

---

[1] Scientific Activities, 1978-79, Applied Research Institute, Ben-Gurion

drought- and salt-resistant plants which stand up to the desert conditions of high solar radiation, salinity and aridity, there is the aim to modify the desert environment itself to suit the needs of conventional agricultural crops and practices. This work is of a long-term nature.

Other recent projects have included the development of Jojoba, which is resistant to drought and salt, and which produces high quality wax suitable for pharmaceuticals, high pressure lubricants, fine chemicals and cosmetics. This shrub, which grows wild in the deserts of Mexico, Arizona and California, was introduced into Israel in the early 1960's, but intensive research on it did not start until 1973; it produces nutlets which yield a high percentage (50% dry weight) of very fine quality liquid wax. A 125 acre commercial plantation has been established near Beersheba and 70 acres of small experimental plots have been set up in arid areas and areas of moderate rainfall. Propagation by cuttings is now well advanced and suitable for application on a large scale; tissue culture techniques have been developed; the significant response of the shrub to irrigation and fertilisers is being further studied; also the breeding of shrubs suitable in shape for mechanical harvesting. Commercial outlets for cosmetic preparations are being explored.[2] Besides the excellent prospects of markets for the oil itself, there is a strong demand for the seed of the improved strains.

Twenty-five lines of Guayule, a plant producing natural rubber latex, have been established under moderate irrigation. This could prove a valuable alternative source of natural rubber. Laboratory investigations have been done to improve techniques of rubber

---

University of the Negev, Introduction, p 1.

[2] Ibid., pp 49-56.

extraction.[3]

Cultivation of the Pistachio nut tree is being investigated in the central Negev highlands, possibly using sewage water for irrigation. Seedlings have also been supplied to the Desert Research Institute in Sede Boqer for the extension of plantations in the central Negev mountains.[4]

Experiments with brackish water irrigation have led to the selection of salt-tolerant tomatoes and further trials with the ten selected varieties. Onions grown with part fresh water and part brackish water gave good results. Certain asparagus strains gave improved results with brackish water, likewise varieties of celery, lettuce, red beet and gladiolus. Drought-resistant plants for landscaping and gardening have been successfully grown in many areas. As a result a number of hardy, strongly drought-resistant plants are available for more remote landscaping and for road embankments where no irrigation is possible.

Valuable work has been done in the introduction of drought-resistant fodder crops to improve the Negev vegetation. Twenty years of trials have resulted in a range of species best suited to the Negev conditions, of good palatability and a ready ability to recover after grazing. There is now the prospect of much improved pasture conditions with a great capacity to overcome the unstable, harsh, conditions of the region.[5] Raw municipal garbage applications have increased the yields of some of these fodder crops by 200-400%. The search goes on, worldwide, for other species which could be usefully introduced into a desert environment.

---

[3] Ibid., p 57.

[4] Ibid., p 65.

[5] Ibid., pp 68-69.

A trial with sea water irrigation was conducted at Eilat on the Red Sea coast. Thirty-six species, mostly plants common to coastal areas or salt marshes, were irrigated with undiluted sea water with a complete fertiliser mixture added; 25 species survived, some growing extremely well. Fodder species which gave a high yield of dry matter and protein showed that sea water can be used for the irrigation of certain terrestrial plants.

Solar energy for heating greenhouses has been the subject of study for many years. A 240 square-metre greenhouse of special design has been built at the Institute; this has a roof with two clear layers of polyethylene; water is circulated between the two transparent layers, absorbing the solar heat by day. From the roof, the heated water is led through plastic pipes beneath the soil and then back to the roof in a closed circuit, having transferred the solar heat to the soil and to a reservoir which stores it. A circulation pump controlled by a thermostat can maintain a moderate temperature of 20°C by day and 10°C by night, when the warm water reservoir is drawn upon for heating the greenhouse.[6]

Research topics include the development of high grade tomato strains which have proved successful and of great value for export. New species, which are salt-tolerant and specially suited to intensive cultivation in desert areas, in enclosed systems, have been produced. Their flavour is improved by irrigation with brackish water. The pioneering production of tomatoes in greenhouses in the eastern Sinai by the Yamit settlements established a strong market in the United Kingdom.

Eucalyptus species are gaining in importance as forest and landscape trees: reafforestation and desert management programmes are expanding; this work is also aimed at providing

---

[6] Ibid., pp 59-60.

an alternative energy source. Ten different species of this and other ornamental trees have been planted in many areas of the northern Negev and throughout Israel.[7]

Recent developments at the Institute have been research projects on plants as a direct source of fuel, new subtropical fruit and nut-tree export crops to be grown in the Arava Valley and other parts of the Negev, and seaweed production for food and protein.

DESERT RESEARCH IN THE CENTRAL NEGEV

The second organisation working in this field is the Jacob Blaustein Institute for Desert Research, 55 km to the south at Sede Boqer in the central Negev. There are special arrangements for collaboration with all the universities of Israel and with others in Europe and America. It is the aim of the government of Israel that the Sede Boqer Institute should become the national centre for all desert research studies in arid zone settlement. It is also intended that the Negev population of about 250,000, should be doubled.

It is planned that a highly qualified staff of scientists and engineers should work on 'interdisciplinary projects in the fields of hydrology, meteorology, desert architecture, solar energy for heating and cooling, growing algae for protein feed and for old, desert ecosystems, raising of the new types of livestock, nomadism and the control of diseases of desert wildlife'.[8]

It is also the aim of this institute to study and develop the

---

[7] Ibid., p 61.

[8] Second Annual Scientific Report, Ben-Gurion University of the Negev, the Institute for Desert Research, Sede Boqer Campus, December 1979, pp 5-6.

natural resources of the Negev: its wide open spaces (60% of the land surface of Israel); its continuously available solar energy; its groundwater resources amounting to between 50 and 100 billion cubic metres; its floodwaters and mineral deposits. The Negev is regarded as an area that can provide for expansion, for industrial development, recreation and tourism, agricultural settlements using groundwater for irrigation and the winter sun for the controlled growth of valuable cash crops for export. An economic concept of the interrelationships in resource development in the region will be evolved: a new Faculty in the University will gradually emerge, a School of Desert Studies; an international centre as

> a meeting-place for the desert researchers of the world, a headquarters where the most prominent scientists in this field will be invited to study. In addition, we foresee it as a focal point for seminars for students from developing countries, where populating the desert and the correct utilisation of its resources form a national problem, just as in Israel. Approximately one-third of the land area of the world is desert or near-desert, and until recently was considered fit only for sparse nomadic tribes. However, because the trend is a rapidly rising population and an increase in industrial pollution, the use of the desert for settlement may become essential.[9]

SCIENTIFIC PROJECTS

Since 1980 there has been a large staff at the Institute, working on various scientific projects, grouped in the six research centres.

---

[9] Ibid., p 9.

1. The Centre for Social Studies

The Nomad Settlement Project has the following major objectives:

1. Investigation of the habits and changing processes of the Bedouin tribes located in the Negev and southern Sinai;

2. Research into manners and adaptation processes of the Bedouin tribes which moved out of the Negev Desert and resettled near Ramla;

3. Participation in a national team which analysed the problems of the Bedouin of the Negev. The team proposed to the Israeli government a general plan for resettling the Bedouin according to the master plan for the development of the Negev. The team was also asked by the government to begin negotiations with the Bedouin leaders regarding the ways and methods of resettlement and the principles of land exchange and compensation.[10]

Experience so far of the Bedouin reactions to urban development in the desert areas has been favourable. Few have settled in Beersheba or in the smaller towns; instead, homogeneous Bedouin settlements have been developed close to towns or in separate small towns. Bedouin men quite readily take up employment in Israeli towns, tending to concentrate in selected places of employment: they make ready use of urban services. There is no evidence that these contacts have brought about any serious conflict in Bedouin society: 'There is no "Bedouin problem" in the

---

[10] Ibid., p 154.

desert towns, and although they lack modern services, the Bedouin settlements appear to retain a certain tough resilience and vitality.' Those who reside away from tribal society ensure that strong links are preserved with relatives on tribal land; they tend to keep small flocks in tribal areas even though they may lose money as a result.[11]

The identity of the tribe still depends on the continued possession of tribal lands with wider access to grazing on the basis of intertribal understandings. As new pressures have been exerted on these areas, nomadic movements have declined and the inducements towards settlement have increased. Besides the attraction of new fields of employment in the towns, there is the strong desire of some Bedouin tribes to have their children educated in modern schools, within their own areas of open settlement and cultivation.

The project is also concerned with the negotiations between the Israeli government and the Bedouin tribes affected by the transfer of military airfields and establishments from Sinai, which constitute a new pressure on tribal areas. As a result a new policy has been developed to compensate the Bedouin for the land they surrender and to ensure them a proper livelihood. 'Furthermore, the details of resettlement are to be negotiated and are not decreed by the State.'[12]

The Unit is also engaged in anthropological investigations in seven Bedouin settled areas, including Tel-Sheva and Ashkelon.

---

[11] Ibid. pp 157-159.

[12] Scientific Activities, Third Annual Report, December 1980, Ben-Gurion University of the Negev, the Jacob Blaustein Institute for Desert Research, p 29.

2. Anthropological Studies of Negev Developing Towns and the Renewal Project of Yeroham

Applied urban research started with a long-term study of the nearby desert town of Yeroham, the smallest and least successful of the existing desert towns, which has been struggling for many years to sustain social and economic growth. Working with local and national authorities and the townspeople, the objective is 'to prepare a comprehensive plan for social development that will make the town a more stable and satisfying community'.[13]

In contrast to Yeroham, Arad, in 1980, was already a flourishing desert town. Very carefully planned, with a balanced disposition of built-up areas and open spaces; with reasonable distances between residential, commercial and municipal centres; spacious attractive gardens; activities for all ages, a high level of services and educational facilities. Immigrants stay and attract others. Economic development in the area provides a good variety of employment.[14]

A comparative study is being done of the reasons for growth and decline of desert development towns, and the social impact of the new air base construction in the Negev.

3. Geostatistics

The Geostatistical Unit is building up a data bank on the Negev to serve as a basis for regional planning. The Unit is drafting a basic atlas of the whole region, presenting all available variables

---

[13] Second Annual Scientific Report, December 1979, Ben-Gurion University of the Negev, the Institute for Desert Research, Sede Boqer Campus, p 153.

[14] Ibid., p 155.

in map form. The university computer will be used to generate automatic mappings for planning purposes.

Before 1948 there was no urban infrastructure in the region. Water shortages restricted agricultural development; also the veteran kibbutzim and moshavim established in earlier years had already developed their own avenues for purchasing and marketing. Social and cultural services were poor and urban planning inadequate. Beersheba, however, developed rapidly after the later sixties into a capital city; first by being named as the capital of the region; by the opening of a large central hospital and the founding of the University; and by being given special capital incentives for industrial development. In the seventies, when it was seen that Beersheba had achieved a state of self-sustaining growth, the financial incentives were switched to the smaller towns forming a single interrelated organisation served by a communications and transportation network specially suited to desert conditions, possibly far removed from the accepted norms of non-arid regions.[15]

The data bank and geostatistical atlas will provide the basic material for 'interdisciplinary research projects to be undertaken by members of the unit and other members of the Institute in fields such as transportation, urban and rural development, diffusion processes, social development'.[16]

During 1980 the administrative sub-regions were mapped, as was the transport network of the Negev. Agricultural and industrial data were collected and analysed, procedures for climatic and archaeological mapping were agreed.

---

[15] Ibid., pp 164-185.

[16] Ibid., pp 173-185.

4. Urban and Regional Planning

The Institute is concerned to protect and preserve the environmental quality of the Negev settlements and development programmes. In the regional and national interests its purpose is to develop, test and apply methods and techniques which avoid permanent disruption of the Negev environmental systems.

The Unit will work on research coordination, liaison with agencies and institutions, and the development of an environmental information system; it will aim at identifying information and research needs; at developing assessment and monitoring methods; finally it will study effective methods of presenting environmental information to planners and decision-makers.[17]

Recent tasks given to the Institute are: definition of the optimum limits of different kinds of human activity that the desert can support, especially in land use and settlement; evaluation of non-renewable and reusable resources; examination of present distribution systems for water, energy, goods and people; priorities for their improvement and development; and, lastly, study of the likely impact of this information and the most simple and direct means for presenting it.[18]

---

[17] Ibid., pp 215-217.

[18] Third Annual Scientific Report, December 1980, Ben-Gurion University of the Negev, the Jacob Blaustein Institute for Desert Research, Sede Boqer Campus, p 42.

5. Resource Economics in Arid Zones

The Economics Research Unit is doing advanced research into agricultural systems, development strategies, marketing problems and the optimum development of water and of economic forecasting.

6. The Centre for Desert Ecology

A strong research staff working on Negev desert ecosystems is seeking a basic understanding of the structure, function and dynamics of the desert, so that human systems can be developed that are as productive as possible, while natural systems are disturbed as little as possible. The desert ecologists urgently need to understand the high sensitivity of the desert ecosystem to human settlement, in view of the potentially serious conflict between conservationist and political interests.

Besides these general studies, the Centre is working on two major interdisciplinary projects:

i) A review and detailed examination of the ecology of a desert watershed, drawing on all relevant work and concentrating on the flow of energy, soil, water and minerals and the interaction between them in a continuously monitored watershed.

ii) A study of the impact of industry on a desert ecosystem; the response of desert vegetation and fauna to air and waterborne pollutants produced by an existing industrial chemical plant.[19]

---

[19] Second Annual Scientific Report, December 1979, Ben-Gurion University of the Negev, the Institute for Desert Research, Sede Boqer Campus, pp 186-211.

A special laboratory is devoted to the physiology of desert plants, their seed dispersal, germination and development; sand dune stabilisation, and forage production from desert plants.

Detailed studies have been made of spatial variations of rainfall; slope and soil characteristics affecting run-off, in which it was established that rainfall on the upper slopes seldom reached the slope base, the contributing area (as in humid regions) being limited to the lower parts of the slope; soil movements; the introduction of new crops; the forecasting of development and harvest dates of a wide variety of crops.[20]

All of this meticulous work is fundamental to the basic understanding of the beneficial use of the Negev Desert for human settlement.

7. The Centre for Water Resource Studies

The Hydrology and Water Resources Engineering project is concerned with the location and characterisation of local water in the desert. It has developed methods for analysing the character of rain and floods and achieving a better understanding of climatological and hydrological processes in the Negev; perhaps also the possibility of identifying the origins of hydrological resources in a desert region. It is also investigating the distribution of salinity, and studying the formation of dew. A programme of mapping and hydrological measurements of water tables in the shallow aquifers of the local alluvial river beds has been completed.[21]

---

[20] Third Annual Scientific Report, December 1980, Ben-Gurion University of the Negev, the Jacob Blaustein Institute for Desert Research, Sede Boqer Campus, pp 53-69.

[21] Second Annual Scientific Report, December 1979, Ben-Gurion University of

The processing of data from all oil and water wells in the Negev shows the existence of substantial aquifers, with 50-100 billion cubic metres of water of varying salinity, likely to provide water for industrial or aquaculture purposes. Studies are being done of the economic feasibility of solar desalination. The distilled water for this would be mixed with primary brackish water to bring the salinity down to an acceptable level for economic use. Detailed studies of this are being undertaken by the Solar Calculation Unit, referred to later.

Improved tree growth has been achieved in microcatchments by sinking small diameter drains into the root-zone. Experiments are being done in nursery plots and in the town of Yeroham. This interesting improvement is also being developed by the experimental run-off farms unit.

Water economy in cotton growing is being developed by drip irrigation using reclaimed sewage, with highly promising results.[22]

8. Experimental Run-off Farms

Many years of research have been devoted to the study of run-off farming, following the brilliant studies by Professor Michael Evenari and others of the ancient Nabatean systems. The Sede Boqer Run-off Farms Unit, headed by Professor Evenari, is continuing this work. The unit operates three experimental farms at Shivta, Avdat and Wadi Mashash; at Avdat there is also a desert garden. Studies are continuing on the determination of the

the Negev, the Institute for Desert Research, Sede Boqer Campus, pp 40-41.

[22] Third Annual Scientific Report, December 1980, Ben-Gurion University of the Negev, the Jacob Blaustein Institute for Desert Research, Sede Boqer Campus, pp 72-73.

relationship between the water contributing area, the catchment size and its character; and the water absorbing area of the farm. Whereas farmers in regions of adequate rainfall welcome the absorption of rain on hillsides, the run-off farmer in arid regions (particularly when rains are concentrated in the winter months) has to encourage the maximum drainage from hillsides so that the water can be collected and allowed to stand on his farm: the water is then absorbed and conserved for growing crops in the summer months. By these means, rainfall of only a few millimetres can be effectively increased by a factor of 30 or more. It is the belief of the Unit that this form of agriculture may help to solve the problems of nomad settlement and to improve agricultural yields in many dry lands of the world.

Work has also been concentrated on microcatchments for flatter areas where the water is moving more slowly and can be directed to support a single fruit tree or shrub in the lowest corner of a square low-cost attachment of less than 1/4 acre. These simple structures are easy to design, build and maintain. Professor Evenari and his group have instructed agricultralists from many countries, notably Pakistan, India, Kenya, Australia, Niger and Burkina Faso; in the last two countries desert areas have become arable.

The unit has continued the search for plants suited for run-off agriculture, including fruit and ornamental trees, pasture plants and field crops. Special attention has been paid to pistachio cultivation, including problems of pollination, disease and pest control; research has started into different rootstocks and the effect of brackish water on pistachio trees grown on the Negev highlands. Root systems of desert plants are being studied in comparison with those of peach, apricot, almond and pistachio trees, all of which have been successfully grown under run-off conditions in the Negev. Kibbutz Sede Boqer is now raising a flock of sheep which will be established on pasture lands watered only by run-off.[23]

The remains of numbers of ancient, quite small, run-off farms in the wadis of the Negev, developed and used by single families, have recently been investigated. Many of these are 1-5 acres in area, irrigated from small dams which were built every few metres along the wadi bed to collect the rainwater and the soil brought down from the hillsides. On each farm there are the remains of a stone house or guard tower and a water cistern. Professor Evenari has instructed an international group of farm managers and agricultural officials on the use of these small watersheds and modern water-harvesting techniques.[24]

During 1980 further contacts were developed with countries having desert conditions similar to those found in the Negev; these included Nigeria, Mexico, the United States, and 'certain Arab States which for obvious reasons will remain unnamed' (a fascinating instance of Israeli-Arab mutual respect and assistance in scientific matters).[25] A further intensive course was arranged for students from the Turkana region of Kenya.

Controlled grazing experiments continued on the areas of run-off pasture with 100 sheep given by the Bedouin: these sheep gained a daily average of just over 100 grams over 90 days. There were six floods in the area which were more than average. More than 1,500 sheep could have been grazed: the harvesting of two

---

[23] Second Scientific Annual Report, December 1979, Ben-Gurion University of the Negev, Sede Boqer Campus, p 35.

[24] Ibid., pp 34-39.

[25] In the course of many visits to the region the writer has observed a number of other genuine instances of Arab-Israeli cooperation, which appears not to be affected by periods of disturbance.

and a half acres of pasture plants yielded over 800 kg of dry matter which could have been preserved for a later bad year. The Unit is studying this possibility of storing excess production from years of higher rainfall to supplement reduced yields in drier years.[26]

9. Desert Meteorology

The work of this unit is concerned with the search for the answer to the question 'What causes deserts?'
- the collection of data (using radar) on winds and clouds in the upper layers of the atmosphere;
- the study of solar radiation in different atmospheric strata; cloud formation and characteristics;
- the study of the varying reflective properties of different ground surfaces (albedo);
- dew formation and distribution: the heat balance near the ground, the properties of desert atmosphere in upper levels;
- the predictability of movements in the desert atmosphere;
- the study of weather and climate modification, for instance by surface albedo changes, by the creation of artificial lakes, by seeding clouds;
- the detailed study of the desertification process;
- the character of rainfall, the localised and very intense Negev storms of short duration and the widespread rainfall of low intensity.

Statistical analysis of rainfall shows a distinct tendency for abnormal extremes of rainfall or drought to persist over periods

---

[26] Third Annual Scientific Report, December 1980, Ben-Gurion University of the Negev, the Jacob Blaustein Institute for Desert Research, Sede Boqer Campus, pp 89-96.

of years, as in the Sahel. Prolonged desiccation alternating with extended periods of exceptional rain suggest that feedback mechanisms may be operating, in which drought promotes drought and heavy rains generate more persistent rainstorms. These effects are accentuated by the extension of human settlement, agriculture and grazing during phases of high rainfall, creating new pressures on vegetation and tree cover; then, with the failure of the rains and increased exposure of surface soil, the return of desiccation processes, the loss of plant cover; the reduction in moisture storage, and increasing wind erosion.

The wider understanding of all these factors should greatly contribute to effective human settlement in the Negev.[27]

One of the least explored aspects of desert meteorology is the occurrence of dew, which can affect the water balance and conditions of growth of desert plants. This may affect the desert ecosystem and new forms of desert agriculture. Dew monitoring at the Institute in Sede Boqer has been in progress since 1977; the conditions for its formation are beginning to be understood, as are its seasonal variations.

Measurements, made in 1980, of albedo changes as moistened soil dried out, showed that it would be possible to determine soil moisture by remote sensing. This must prove to be a most important discovery as it could be accomplished by fixed instrument platforms or by moving ones, such as aircraft or satellites.[28]

---

[27] Second Annual Scientific Report, December 1979, Ben-Gurion University of the Negev, the Institute for Desert Research, Sede Boqer Campus, pp 62-73.

[28] Third Annual Scentific Report, December 1980, Ben-Gurion University of the Negev, the Jacob Blaustein Institute for Desert Research, Sede Boqer Campus, pp 98-104.

10. The Centre for Desert Habitat Studies, Solar Building and Conservation

Research into desert settlement has concentrated on the design and architecture of a desert village for 200 housing units, with supporting services; the establishment of criteria for site selection, orientation, function and form; the study of the role of shade and structures to provide it; the investigation of locally available building materials such as the adobe mud brick used in the first prototype building. A study is to be made of the suitability of subterranean and earth-covered dwellings; the use of ornamental desert plants and vegetation as part of the settlement environment. Ornamental gardens have been designed to be suitable for desert living.[29] Close-planted traditional gardens are first established near to the house, using drip irrigation; this area will then be surrounded by trees to filter out dust from the air and decrease wind velocity, thus decreasing the water demand of the conventional garden surrounding the house. Finally, there will be an outer ring of desert garden using ornamental desert plants resistant to heat and dryness; this area will need irrigation in the early years to enable desert plants to reach their full growth quickly. With the establishment of a favourable microclimate, very little irrigation will be needed. (The work of the Applied Research Institute on drought-resistant plants for landscaping is relevant here.) Work is also being done on reafforestation and desert management programmes, including the search for alternative energy sources.

Studies have been done of the social preparation of inhabitants so as to avoid the shortcomings of some of the desert towns in the

[29] Second Annual Scientific Report, December 1979, Ben-Gurion University of the Negev, the Institute for Desert Research, Sede Boqer Campus, p 119.

northern Negev, established during the last twenty-five years, as opposed to the successful agricultural settlements.

Building climatology research has been concentrated on the solar heating and cooling of buildings; the development of integrated systems in which *the architecture and structure of a building become integral components of an energy system so that the building becomes in effect an 'energy-machine'*; the structural mass itself, or reservoirs of gravel, are used for thermal storage, for the preservation and re-use of cool night temperatures, to cool buildings in daytime, particularly in summer, and to keep the temperature rise within acceptable limits. Equally, excess heat can be absorbed in a way that prevents overheating in daytime and may be released at night or on cloudy days. Heat flow can be achieved passively by natural radiation or convection, or actively by blowing air through a gravel thermal store, using the minimum of energy.

These studies are aimed at identifying the 'least purchased energy designs', the protection of the occupants from climatic extremes by the use of low cost systems, as unsophisticated as possible, to bring conditions within the ranges of temperature, humidity and ventilation beyond which physiological stress begins.[30]

To this end work was done on methods of cooling the structural mass by night ventilation and using the roof as a cooling element by using evaporation and shading. Further work on earth-integrated buildings, with unshaded southern exposure combined with low-cost passive solar heating in winter, makes it possible to approach the point at which solar heating can prove sufficient throughout the year. Complete all-year-round solar

---

[30] Ibid., pp 131-133.

heating and ventilation has been installed in a nearby school and the unit is engaged on the design of a new housing project for 100 houses in Jerusalem and improving the solar qualities of housing in an established desert kibbutz settlement.[31]

11. The Desert Architecture Unit

This unit has the task of formulating and testing new designs for desert habitation. The central project in 1980 was the further improvement of the experimental adobe house, designed jointly with the Applied Solar Calculations Unit. Significant advances have been made in passive solar heating and cooling systems, including the design and construction of an adaptation of the Iranian 'Wind-catch' evaporative cooling system, including the 'Faiman Rotating Prism wall'.

The ancient Persian system consists essentially of two walls set at an angle which can be rotated to face the wind: the resulting stream of air is then led into a tower where it is cooled by evaporating water from hanging surfaces saturated with water.

These improvements, combined with a roof design which has a cross-sectional profile allowing the entry of winter sunlight into northern rooms while excluding the direct summer sun, approach the achievement of a high level of comfort without the use of sophisticated and expensive devices, passive or active, for cooling and heating. The advantages are the use of local materials, with good insulating properties, the employment of normal family skills or reasonably available labour, and the use of simple technology.

---

[31] Third Scientific Annual Report, December 1980, Ben-Gurion University of the Negev, the Jacob Blaustein Institute for Desert Research, Sede Boqer Campus, pp 107-113. (Unfortunately it has not been possible to obtain subsequent reports.)

The unit performs the function of the Institute's resident architect in planning its growth. A 20-year expansion plan is being drawn up; a computer centre has been designed and built, with improved building performance and aesthetic design; shading devices have been developed.[32]

12. The Solar Energy Centre, Applied Solar Calculations

This centre has had a series of projects for the design of solar hot water systems, for improvements in architectural design to reduce winter heating and summer cooling loads with passive solar elements, and the testing and improvement of locally manufactured solar collectors, assessing their properties and undertaking further work in this field calling for a strong theoretical background. Important tasks have been the study of hydroponic (soil-less) systems as part of the work on closed systems of agriculture in the desert regions (to be discussed later); also the maximum use of solar energy in greenhouses. A new project for solar desalination can now produce about five litres of fresh water per day for each square metre of surface area. Research is being done on the possible use of the energy released during condensation to pre-heat incoming saline water, thus creating a new multi-effect type of still.

Work has continued on the design of a house wall incorporating rotating prisms which form a passive heating element. The prism wall allows direct solar gain in the form of slits of light, continuously adjustable in width up to about 15% of the glazing area. By insulating one prism surface with a stick-on substance it is possible to reflect away unwanted summer

---

[32] Ibid., pp 115-126.

radiation. This, combined with venting, should prevent overheating. By rotating the insulated surface out of the way when it is not required, and allowing the stored heat to enter the building, the heat storage problem is at least partially solved, in an elegant and economic way.[33]

A further refinement is that by the use of hollow columns (for liquid storage) the thermal mass can be varied by using different liquids. Altogether, by design, construction and orientation, the best advantages can be made of local weather conditions and solar radiation to ensure that the interior is warm in winter and cool in summer.

The Solar Energy Centre has also been concerned with the energy available from saline solar ponds, in particular the prototype electricity power station which is generating 150kw from an area of 7,000m^2 in the Dead Sea, using a new type of turbine operating at temperatures below 100°C.

A major research and development effort is also being made in the field of direct generation of electricity from solar radiation, particularly in the search for a cost-effective solar cell. Work is also being done on the indirect process of converting solar radiation into heat, to drive turbines.

13. Biotechnology and Desert Agriculture, Closed System Agriculture

A large group of scientists studied closed systems of agriculture. The first projects included the development of a model liquid optical filter greenhouse; this has been designed to produce high yields with a low water requirement by the storage of surplus

---

[33] Ibid., pp 128-137.

solar energy during the day for release at night. The experimental greenhouse also has a double layer of polythene through which a liquid is circulated, drawing off the hot day temperature for storage and later use at night; so transferring surplus solar energy from day to night. This approach is also being used in the development of a new, closed, hydroponics system. Finally, the design and trial of a new type of desalinating roof for a closed system has been started. It is likely that a sub-project for the supply of carbon dioxide gas will be added to these extremely interesting projects: this could lead to greatly increased productivity.

The greatest importance is attached to the development of closed systems for very efficient and economical irrigation; the high humidity, closed, atmosphere reduces plant water use by a factor of 5 to 10 as the water transpired by plants is recycled; the use of solar heating and cooling to remove the extremes of temperature saves conventional fuels; carbon dioxide sup-plementation becomes feasible; and so optimum growing conditions can be provided throughout most of the year. It has also been found that the CO_2 rich atmosphere in these systems reduces the sensitivity of some plants to salinity and introduces the possibility of the use of small quantities of brackish groundwater. In addition, wind damage and sand abrasion are prevented, pest and disease control are simplified, and plant nutrition can be automatically programmed.

It is the expert view that water used in the closed system will be one-fifth to one-tenth of that in an open field in the same desert region and that a trained farmer will need about 1/20th of the conventionally irrigated acreage to earn his living. Consequently, water consumption for each settled family would be 1% to 2% of the water needed for open field, conventional, irrigated desert agriculture.[34] This is a very remarkable achievement. Although the forecast relates to the most advanced Israeli farmers operating in the most favourable circumstances, it is an indication of the performance which will be achieved by many other farming communities in the Middle East who are rapidly adopting modern methods. These advances will eventually have a dramatic effect on the absorptive capacity of the land in other arid and semi-arid zones.

In 1980 work was continued on the solar desalination sub-project associated with closed systems agriculture. Together, these two projects are seen as a means of reducing fresh water requirements for farming in arid regions. Instead of large volumes of fresh water this need will be met by a solar still with a small volume of fossil water, supplemented by fresh water gathered from the roof of the closed system itself. The project scientists forecast that only $100m^3$ of brackish water, with the collected rainfall, and only $100m^3$ from the solar still should provide all the agricultural requirements of an arid zone farmer. 'The same farmer, using conventional irrigated agriculture, would need at least four hectares (10 acres) to make a reasonable living, requiring about $60,000m^3$ of relatively fresh water.'[35] Three variants of a prototype still are being used.

---

[34] Second Annual Scientific Report, December 1979, Ben-Gurion University of the Negev, the Institute for Desert Research, Sede Boqer Campus, pp 74-80.

[35] Third Annual Scientific Report, December 1980, Ben-Gurion Universtiy of the Negev, the Jacob Blaustein Institute for Desert Research, Sede Boqer Campus, pp 139-150.

14. Applied Hydrobiology

The work now being done by the Applied Hydrobiology Unit in studying the growth of algae is likely to be of far-reaching importance. It seems probable that algae will prove to be a valuable economic product with applications in food production, animal feed, and as a possible energy source.

Arid desert areas offer important advantages for the cultivation of algae. The very conditions which impose severe limitations on conventional agriculture are specially favourable for this: saline water, high daytime and low night temperatures, high levels of solar radiation and wide areas of available land with inadequate rainfall. Besides being tolerant to brackish water, or even sea water, algae have other distinct advantages over conventional crops. They can be grown in continuous culture under controlled conditions, in artificial ponds most favourable for the absorption and use of solar irradiance. A further advantage is that the entire plant body of the algae can be harvested and used, as water plants do not have to divert resources for the growth of purely structural material such as root systems for anchorage, or frameworks of branches to carry foliage.

Still another advantage of algae culture is that the nutrient requirements may be easily maintained at optimal level. Clearly, three classes of plant nutrients are distinguishable: mineral elements, carbon dioxide and water. If one of these factors is not optimally available, the growth of the plant is limited. Thus, production of plant biomass depends on defining and alleviating the limiting factors for growth and development. In algae it is readily possible to maintain growth conditions in which there is no nutrient limitation. By comparison, the growth of well-watered and well-nourished field agricultural plants, exposed to high irradiance, is soon limited by shortage of CO_2. In contrast, bicarbonate and CO_2 can easily be introduced into the algae medium to alleviate carbon limitation to growth.[36]

Although presently not economic for protein production, the potential of this method of bio-production is very promising for special products, and might in due course yield protein-rich foods. This may reflect a revolution in plant production through the use of species and systems which differ greatly from those currently accepted in agriculture.

A consistent effort towards optimisation of algal biomass production, harvesting and product processing, as well as genetic engineering and basic research to better comprehend relevant biosynthetic pathways will yield, step by step, biotechnologies of significant economic importance. This would seem particularly useful in arid lands in which populations are malnourished, and yet cultivation of plants by conventional methods is severely handicapped.[37]

Semi-commercial ponds are being operated at Sede Boqer for algal biomass production. These cover an area of $200m^2$; the water is artificially stirred so that the algae are exposed to a continuous light/dark cycle during the day. The effect of short periods of exposure to light in the upper layers of the pond, alternating with long periods of darkness in deeper layers, increases the yield per unit area and the economic feasibility. For any concentration of algae, an increase in turbulence results in an increase in the specific growth rate.[38]

---

[36] Second Annual Scientific Report, December 1979, Ben-Gurion University of the Negev, the Institute of Desert Research, Sede Boqer Campus, p 85.

[37] Ibid., p 87.

[38] Ibid., p 107.

Problems remain in developing the most suitable economic properties of algae and in solving the problems or harvesting and processing it. The search goes on for algae of increased economic value; as additives for human food; feed for fish to increase fish farming; and for the production of fuel oil. Great advances have been made and there is little reason to doubt that this work will prove of profound importance to the peoples of the arid zones in the future.

15. Applied Geobotany and Desert Agriculture

The Applied Geobotany Unit is preparing an Agro-Ecological map of the Negev in conjunction with botanists of the Field School at Sede Boqer. The Unit is also working on a study of the Ecogeographical regions of the plant world and a plan for the establishment of a world desert botanical garden. It studies plants such as succulents and cacti which are attractive and make economical use of water; plants for export; plants representative of the hot deserts of the world for the desert botanical collection; the selection of plants suitable for industry, medicine, food and grazing and for the stabilisation of sand dunes. The Unit will also study the improvement of established plants such as pistachios and almonds.[39]

16. Comparative Medicine and Animal Physiology in Arid Zones

A start has been made in the building of a Large Animal Research Centre: this will have the most modern veterinary research

---

[39] Third Annual Scientific Report, December 1980, Ben-Gurion University of the Negev, the Jacob Blaustein Institute for Desert Research, Sede Boqer Campus, p 162.

facilities in the Middle East, 'capable of working on comparative medical problems of arid zones in animals ranging in size from a mouse to a camel'.[40] Further work will be done in the breeding of pure-bred Arab horses; work will also be done in the study and breeding of Dorper sheep from South Africa, which are believed to be very suitable for the conditions of the Negev. The camel research programmes will be extended, also the study of the Canaani dog.

Finally, the Institute is concerned with the need for environmental education on a national scale. At present, the response of the educational institutes to the spectacular progress in ecosystem ecology has not been satisfactory. It will be the task of the Unit to publicise this work: to see that curriculum development keeps pace with the research findings; to develop an in-service teachers' education programme in collaboration with the Environmental Education Centre at Midreshat Sede Boqer; and to develop a course for English-speaking students to be available at a college in Yeroham.[41]

A NEW DESERT CIVILISATION IN THE MAKING

This programme is remarkable for its very wide range and depth; its scientific quality is probably unsurpassed anywhere.

The benefits of this work will extend far beyond Israel itself. There could be lasting mutual advantages to Israel and the Arab world in the development of desert areas and in future

---

[40] Ibid., p 164.

[41] Second Annual Scientific Report, December 1979, Ben-Gurion University of the Negev, the Institute for Desert Research, Sede Boqer Campus, pp 218-223.

collaboration in industrial development. Research projects in a number of these fields, and others, are in progress in Saudi Arabia, Egypt, Abu Dhabi, Bahrain and Syria. Solar energy research and development in Jordan was started in 1972. The Royal Scientific Society of Jordan has an increasing range of research agreements with other national and international bodies in the field of solar energy.[42] Valuable technology in desert management will also become available to supplement the work being done in the Arab world and in other desert areas further afield. Especially important are the contributions which this work could make in assisting the oil-rich Arab countries in developing their longer range and more permanent economies after the decline of their oil resources.

All of those working for the resolution of the Arab-Israeli conflict should be encouraged by the knowledge that, if peace can be achieved, there are extraordinary possibilities of building a new and more enduring civilisation for all the peoples of the Middle East.

---

[42] Royal Scientific Society, Solar Energy Activities at the Mechanical Engineering Department, prepared by Dr. F.A. Daghestani and others, Amman, Jordan, March 1981, pp 24-25.

5

THE DECISIVE IMPORTANCE OF IRRIGATION WATER IN A MIDDLE EAST SETTLEMENT

Long before the Arab-Israeli wars the sharing of water supplies was seen to be as important as the fair distribution of land between the two peoples.

Those wars led to the abandonment of the proposals made nearly 60 years before to use the Jordan waters for the benefit of all riparian owners, now the countries of Syria, Jordan and Israel; to use the Sea of Galilee as a natural reservoir and to lead into it the abundant and very pure waters of the Yarmouk river, perhaps also to introduce surplus water from the Litani river into the Jordan headwaters, in return for hydroelectric power to be transmitted back to Lebanon. The result has been new plans for the diversion of the Yarmouk river to serve the eastern Jordan valley independently of the Sea of Galilee and the quite separate development by Israel of the Jordan river headwaters.

Before the loss of the West Bank, in June 1967, the government of Jordan had plans to lead a part of the Yarmouk water under the river Jordan so that extensive irrigation and rural development could be undertaken. West Bank prospects have been drastically reduced by the loss of this vital low salinity water. The river Jordan, below the Sea of Galilee, is now too saline for normal agricultural purposes, and water supplies for the dedicated and very skilful Arab farmers of the West Bank are being further reduced by the increasing use of other water resources by the

Israeli settlements in the area. A solution of this problem must be an essential part of a plan for a Middle East peace by the creation of a viable Palestinian Arab administration combining the West Bank and an enlarged Gaza Strip. Ideally this administration would be self-governing and in close collaboration with neighbouring countries: the revival of the original West Bank allocation of the Yarmouk water would then make possible the resettlement of up to 250,000 refugees for whom there could be no other major reception area in the region. Recent developments in the East Jordan valley have an important bearing on this problem.

THE JORDAN VALLEY AUTHORITY IRRIGATION PROJECT

This important project area is situated in the north-west corner of the Hashemite Kingdom, to the south of the Yarmouk river, in a continuous strip of irrigable land along the east bank of the river Jordan which varies in width from four to nine kilometres. Small in comparison with many irrigation projects, this development is the resourceful response of the Hashemite Kingdom to the difficult and restrictive circumstances of the region. The project should be completed with the ultimate development of 41,000 hectares of irrigated land; the annual supply of 47 million cubic metres of water for municipal and industrial purposes in Irbid and the Jordan valley; and hydroelectric power plants with a capacity of 40 Megawatts.[1]

At this final stage of development, the present irrigation

---

[1] Jordan Valley Authority: Jordan Valley Irrigation Project, Feasibility Study, Vol I, Main Report, II-1.

resources of the Yarmouk river would be employed to the maximum extent. The major storage dam at Maqarin could eventually regulate the Yarmouk river flow. Depending on international political developments in the region, the full benefit of the Yarmouk river will only be realised when peace negotiations make possible the construction of a diversion dam at Adasiye where the opposite north bank of the river now forms part of the Israeli-occupied Golan Heights.[2]

The final total of just over 41,000 hectares of irrigated land will be mainly commanded by the East Ghor Main Canal, 94.5 km long. 36,000 hectares of this total are allocated: the final stage of the project includes a reserved and still not allocated area of irrigation, described as 'sprinkler irrigation facilities, including mainline conveyance, for 5,147 hectares'. Presumably, if political developments were favourable, this development could be allocated to the West Bank. Included in the 36,000 hectares are areas to be irrigated from the Yarmouk river above the diversion and a number of side wadis with common areas above the main canal; these are likely to total 3,197 hectares. Although a small proportion of the whole, they illustrate the great skill and ingenuity that has been applied in achieving the maximum possible irrigated area in the East Jordan valley.

---

[2] Ibid., IV-23. The Maqarin Reservoir will have a useful storage volume of 275 million cubic metres of water: it will prove of immense value in drought periods such as that of recent years, particularly 1979.

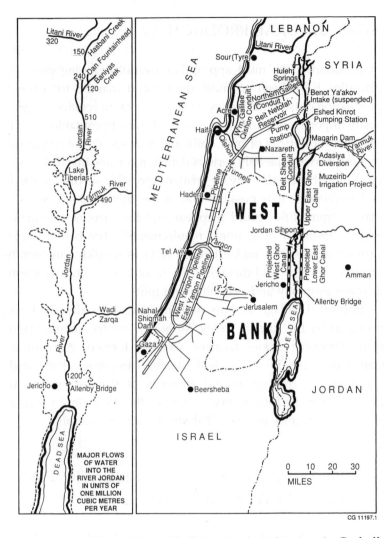

Adapted from *The Jordan Valley Plan*, by Maurice A. Garhell.
Copyright © March 1965 by Scientific American, Inc.
All rights reserved

AGRICULTURAL PRODUCTION

In considering the most appropriate overall cropping plan, the priorities have been to meet domestic demands; to estimate production outside the Valley Authority area; to replace the most costly imports; and, finally, to expand the most profitable exports. The present deficits of fruit, milk and beef should be eliminated by now, leaving the only serious deficit in cereals; this deficit will most probably be offset by far greater exportable surpluses of fruit and vegetables. It is possible that in the later 1990's 'deficits in many commodities could reappear and the surplus production will be absorbed by national requirements'.[3] The benefits from agricultural research and extension services should, however, be apparent by now and this will lead to continuing improvements in water economy and agricultural output.

Improved village layouts and amenities are already being provided by the Jordan Valley Authority; modern marketing is being encouraged and farmers' societies formed. Agricultural standards, already high, will steadily improve. This wide experience of the agricultural economy of the area would be invaluable in the future development of the West Ghor Canal as an essential facility in a new Palestinian administration.

THE ISRAEL EXPERIENCE OF IRRIGATION AND SCIENTIFIC WATER ECONOMY

Early in its history the Government of Israel had to tackle the problems of basic, natural inequalities of water distribution in

---

[3] Ibid., VI-12.

which 85% of the total water potential was in the north while 50% of the irrigable land was in the south.[4]

The resultant plan was of decisive importance. It involved the use of the Sea of Galilee as the national reservoir; water drawn from it was augmented by ground water from the coastal areas and surplus water from smaller rivers to supply the National Water Carrier; this by-passes the West Bank to provide for irrigation further south; and finally, in the Negev, all un-committed water is used with the maximum economy. At the same time economy in water usage is being studied to discover the maximum salinity that each crop and each soil type can tolerate; salt tolerant strains of various crops are being successfully bred; studies are continuing of the conditions under which undesirable limits of salinity may build up in the soil. Research continues into the precise needs of crops at each stage of development so that supplementary irrigation schemes can be designed exactly to match those needs. Overhead spraying, which is economic and flexible, is widely used; drip systems have further increased water economy; new methods of sub-soil irrigation have been studied with remarkable results — they have reduced water usage to half that of overhead spraying. These studies are leading to improved precision and economy in irrigation. Efforts are also being made to encourage the more efficient use of water by all other users, including local government; by automatic rationing systems; by efficient cooling plants in factories and sponsored planning of production units that economise in water; by the re-use of treated sewage in industry and vigilance over it to

---

[4] Arid Zone Research XXIII, Agricultural Planning and Village Community in Israel, edited by Joseph Ben-David, UNESCO, 1964.

prevent the pollution of sources.[5]

In 1975 the overall water allocations in Israel were:

	(million cubic metres)
Agriculture	1325
Industry	95
Municipal Services	300
TOTAL	1720[6]

There is very little prospect of substantial new resources being found and the Israel government is turning now to large scale sewage reclamation.

The Southern Project[7] of the government of Israel will use treated sewage water to develop a new settlement region in the south of Israel. It will now include part of the Negev in the place of the Sinai area which formed part of the original project, until the 1979 Egyptian-Israeli peace treaty.

Two types of farming were planned. Controlled Environment Agriculture is a recent advance in intensive production of export crops of tomatoes, peppers and melons by creating special growth conditions in glass-houses taking advantage of the very favourable environment of the Negev/ Sinai area. These include the soil conditions; the intensity of radiation; temperatures, and lack of

---

[5] Israel Government Year Book, 5731 (1970/71), p 53.

[6] Kidma, Israel Journal of Development, No 10/1977 (Vol 3, No 2), p 5. (Article by Saul Arlosoroff, Israel Deputy Water Commissioner.)

[7] Following the withdrawal of Israel from Sinai, this whole scheme is subject to major revision to conform to the pre-1967 southern boundary of Israel; it is also subject to financial stringency arising from the priority being given to settlements in the West Bank.

frost which together make it possible to use glass-houses without heating or artificial lighting. The family farming unit will be three dunams of glass-houses; drip irrigation will be employed which will introduce fertiliser and controls to keep down weeds and plant diseases. The production of export tomatoes per dunam (a quarter of an acre) is 20 tons grown in two main crops: besides the export quality there are five tons a year for local markets.[8]

The other farm type will be for the production of basic crops by Advanced Technology Agriculture. The proposed crops are wheat, corn, sorghum, perhaps peanuts and other oil crops. The whole project is long-term. It depends on attracting specially able second generation settlers and will not reach full production capacity in much less than fifteen years.

THE STUDY OF COASTAL GROUNDWATER HORIZONS IN THE GAZA STRIP AND THE ADJACENT PARTS OF SINAI

This area could benefit from studies of sea water irrigation and the salt water/fresh water interface similar to those carried out along the coastal plain of Israel by the Hydrological Service of the Israel government.

A substantial volume of water (70 million m^3) is earmarked from the National Water Carrier for the recharge of coastal groundwater in Israel: work is also being done in collecting and storing stormwater long enough for it to percolate into the coastal subsoil. These measures have been successful in lowering the

---

[8] The Southern Project. A proposal for the Development of a Rural Region in the South of Israel. Dr Ra'anan Weitz, Jerusalem, October 1975, pp 2-4 and 12-20.

interface between fresh and salt water, by restraining the undercutting pressures of sea water.[9] The Shiqma storage dam immediately to the north of the Gaza Strip is an excellent example of these works. It should be possible to build a similar dam in the Nahal Besor Valley to the great benefit of ground water resources in the Gaza Strip; a 4,000 acre flood-reservoir is planned close to the eastern boundary of the Strip.[10] This scheme could be included in any plans for development in the area, possibly as a joint measure to benefit both Israel and a new Palestinian administration.

The rainfall of 400mm at the eastern end of the Gaza Strip diminishes rapidly towards the south and west, so that at Rafah it is erratic and below 150mm with arid conditions fully established. Ground water reserves are large; but these are being over-pumped and there is a serious risk that this supply will become increasingly saline through the seepage of sea water. In all, there are 1,200 wells, yielding 65 million cubic metres of water annually. Experts advise that pumping should be reduced by half and that this reduction should be particularly urged in the southern half of the Strip where the salination threat is greatest.[11]

---

[9] Geography of Israel. New Revised edition, by Ephraim Orni and Elisha Efrat. Israel University Press, 1973, pp 452-455.

[10] Ibid., p 45.

[11] Ibid., pp 392-393.

THE DESALINATION POSSIBILITIES IN THE GAZA/SINAI COASTAL REGION

It has long been the hope of mankind to transform deserts and arid regions. It is fast becoming an urgent necessity. Nowhere is it more urgent than in the Gaza/Sinai region to bring arid coastal land into productive use and settlement. There is also an abundance of relevant skill and experience in very economical conventional irrigation, in the immediate neighbourhood. Brackish water is widely available in the eastern Sinai coastal area. Desalination techniques are well established for the treatment of both brackish (and sea) water: for the lower degree of salinity in brackish water (up to one fifth of sea water) reverse osmosis is the most economical system; it is a refined filtration process using semi-permeable membrane filters which allow the passage of water molecules and prevent the passage of molecules of dissolved substances. Real costs of desalination are falling with the steady improvement of processes. A pilot project using reverse osmosis might soon be a desirable step. Meanwhile if land can be ceded (or leased) by Egypt to allow a small 144 square miles westwards extension of the Gaza Strip, settlements would be in an area where brackish ground water should be sufficient for an initial small number of agricultural settlers.

The process of resettlement cannot be simple either in the West Bank or in the hoped-for extension of the Gaza Strip. The problem in the West Bank (assuming that political developments make possible the allocation of water from the Yarmouk river) would be the resettlement of refugee families from the UNRWA camps in Lebanon, Syria, Jordan and the West Bank. The gradual absorption of up to 250,000 Palestinians (half on the land) presents formidable problems. Besides the use of the vital Yarmouk river water, there might be the need to reorganise the use of about 70 wells in the Jordan valley and the supplies from springs, mainly in the Jericho area, yielding altogether more than 60 million cubic metres of water a year. All of this water is suitable for highly productive irrigation in the natural greenhouse conditions of the Jordan valley. Establishing the ownership of land, after the passage of two generations and the rationalisation of land holdings for intensive irrigation and settlement, must take time and most probably some temporary transitional camps would be needed. There would arise also the problem of settling families whose original homes were elsewhere than on the West Bank but who wish to be settled in that area. Some of the most difficult and urgent claims will arise from the extremely serious dislocation of Palestinian society in Lebanon.

The problems of resettlement in a possible westward extension of the Gaza Strip are more technological than social. Here Palestinian society is probably more technologically advanced and less disrupted by recent hostilities. Less geographical movement is involved and far greater chances exist of developing settlements as a rural extension of the predominantly urban society.

Despite the Arab-Israeli hostilities extending over more than forty years there have been impressive economic and social developments in the area. Spectacular advances have been made in agriculture — and especially in irrigation — which have greatly increased the absorptive capacity of the land. There is land in the West Bank and adjoining the Gaza Strip which could be brought into productive settlement by the use of accessible water resources and the use of new and proven desalination methods. Great progress has taken place in Palestinian agriculture and there is no doubt that the Palestinians have the capacity to develop a settled and prosperous society in the conditions that could be provided.

97

6

THE MOUNTING POPULATION AND POLITICAL PRESSURES IN THE WEST BANK

Shortly after the Camp David negotiations the Israeli government gave assurances that there would be no further increase in the numbers of Israeli settlements in the Occupied Territories. At that time the estimated West Bank total was 68. In 1983 a total of 167 settlements was planned, in breach of those assurances. Military settlements have been converted to civilian kibbutzim. Vast sums have been spent by the Housing Ministry in 'building cities and urban settlements'; settlers' housing has been heavily subsidised; state land in the West Bank has been sold very cheaply. Israeli companies setting up in the West Bank have been guaranteed against the possibility of future evacuation by the establishment of a special government fund, but at the same time companies were told that withdrawal will not take place. Six large new settlements have industrial zones. The largest Israeli film studios have been built in the West Bank ten miles from Jerusalem.[1] These developments have been publicised by official public service broadcasting. There are fewer orthodox Jewish settlers coming forward and the recent official appeals have attracted numbers of young artisan, and other, families who have been unable to find housing in Israel itself. Heavily subsidised housing close to the western boundary of the West Bank enables these

---

[1] The Times, 25 January 1983.

98

settlers to commute daily to their work in Israel. The drive to expand Israeli settlement in the West Bank has led to civil unrest; the stoning of security vehicles and reprisals against Palestinians in the neighbourhood; the closing of schools and universities; collective punishments; and the prevention of agricultural exports. There have also been serious disturbances in the larger centres.

This headlong increase in Israeli settlement in the West Bank has constituted a double threat. It made it impossible to conduct any fruitful discussion about Palestinian autonomy. Without such a prospect there can be no approach to an enduring solution of the Arab-Israeli conflict; it also increases the population imbalance within Israel itself.

The Israeli anxieties about the security of their country are very real. There is a clear case for a limited number of strategic Israeli settlements in the West Bank, as part of the negotiation of recognised and genuinely secure boundaries for the state of Israel. The experience of the Sinai withdrawal suggests that regional security should be possible on the basis of the very efficient early warning systems used there; a small fraction of the numbers of Israeli settlements that exist today; demilitarisation and firm international guarantees; and even some reduction in Israel's extraordinary military power.

The intense development of the West Bank settlements also imposes an excessively heavy strain on Israel's economy; it leads to the neglect of conventional agriculture within Israel itself; it causes a diversion of scarce human resources needed in Israel. Many of the present settlements are small and only in the early stages of development, but they are heavily armed and form a network of a military presence, designed to ensure close military control of the entire West Bank. The increasing numbers of civil and military settlements in the West Bank have greatly reduced the water resources throughout the Jordan valley. Deep wells have been drilled, lowering the water table, reducing the yield of the shallower Palestinian wells, and reducing the chances of expanding Arab agriculture; preventing, also, any substantial refugee resettlement in the future (unless water can be brought from the Yarmouk or Litani rivers). There is no prospect that the highly intelligent and able Palestinian people could embark on the development of autonomy, and possible further constitutional progress, under the shadow of such a comprehensive military occupation.

The World Zionist Organisation forecast an increase in the Israeli civil, West Bank, population to 100,000 by 1987. This rate of settlement would have brought the Israeli proportions to 10.7% by the end of 1987, assuming that no significant numbers of Palestinians left the West Bank and that their rate of natural increase was maintained.

The Jewish minorities are declining in the Northern district of Israel. In this district, at the end of 1981, lived 320,000 Jews and 304,500 non-Jews. The critical point of population equality of the two groups was very close, as 68% of the non-Jewish inhabitants were under 25 years of age compared with 52% among the Jewish population. There were no signs of renewed large-scale Jewish immigration into Israel or its Northern district.

The acceleration of Israeli settlement in the West Bank announced by the World Zionist Organisation has mainly been achieved with funds provided by the government of the United States and from private resources there. The increased pressure of Israeli urban and rural settlements might drive out some of the Palestinian population.

A way of avoiding generations of deepening and fruitless conflict might be to explore the proposals for reconciliation by Dr.

Ra'anan Weitz, published in the New York Times in 1983. Dr. Weitz was a member of the World Zionist Organisation Executive and head of the rural settlement department of the Jewish Agency for more than 20 years. These proposals were:

1. To speed up the autonomy negotiations into a shorter transitional stage.

2. During this time, Dr. Ra'anan Weitz declared, 'Israel must work with the people living in the occupied territories to carry out development programmes for the absorption of 100,000 refugees, now spread throughout the Arab world, in the West Bank and the Gaza Strip. Water can be brought from the Litani river, in Lebanon, to arid regions in the West Bank and the Gaza Strip suitable for the development of agriculture. Settlement activities will have to be undertaken by the refugees themselves, and compensation must be paid to the owners of any land reallocated in the process. Eventually, these development programmes will facilitate the growth of new industry and agricultural services that can help to support additional population. This, in turn, will stimulate urban development.'

3. This would open the way to a permanent solution, requiring similar settlement projects on the part of the Arab countries where Palestinian refugees are now living.

4. The approach to the setting up of a Palestinian administration in the West Bank and Gaza Strip must, in any permanent solution, include 'a Jewish-settlement barrier extending along the Jordan river and constituting a part of the State of Israel.

Only such a barrier can ensure Israeli security through a practical and permanent demilitarisation of the West Bank without the need of paper assurances.' Dr. Weitz then outlined three possible solutions.

First: 'an agreement with Jordan' by which the West Bank and the Gaza Strip could be included in Jordan in any form or manner that Jordanians and Palestinians agreed upon.

A second possibility is a federative union between Israel and the Arab districts in the West Bank and Gaza Strip. Such a state would be composed of eight districts: five with a clear Jewish majority and three with a clear Arab majority. Jerusalem, itself a separate district, would be the capital city and the seat of the central government.

Each district would elect a fixed and equal number of representatives to the federal parliament This body would elect a central government that would oversee the security and foreign relations of the state – which might be called Eretz Israel (Palestine). The internal affairs of each district, such as development projects, immigration, education, health, social welfare, religious affairs, etc., would be relegated to local governments elected by regional councils.

A third option is the establishment of a Palestinian state through the union of the West Bank and the Gaza Strip into one political unit, enjoying full rights except for the establishment of an army and the acquisition of heavy weaponry. In this case, the existence of an Israeli-settlement barrier along the Jordan would be particularly important to ensure the permanent demilitarisation of the Palestinian state in all possible future political upheavals.

No matter which permanent solution were chosen, Israel's Arab citizens could, if they wish, belong to one of the Arab districts without having to change their place of residence. The same would apply to the Jews who chose to live in an Arab district. There would be no need to transfer settlements or exchange populations.

These proposals are very important, coming from the pre-eminent Israel authority on the techniques of rural settlement so highly placed in the World Zionist Organisation and the Jewish Agency. For this reason they have been reproduced in full. They provide a basis for realistic negotiation. Possibly the scale of Palestinian resettlement on the West Bank could be increased above the level proposed by Dr. Weitz. There is no means of judging the extent to which Palestinians would accept resettlement in their present host countries; considerable numbers have been acceptably re-established, particularly in Jordan.

Dr. Weitz has stressed that the present opportunity for a peaceful outcome of the Arab-Israeli conflict depends on a fair and permanent solution of the Palestinian problem which can only be achieved through 'painful compromises by both parties'.

In recent years the pressures have increased. In the 'uprising' during 1988 over 300 Palestinians were killed. During 1989, 90 of the 98 West Bank schools were unable to function properly; UNRWA was extremely concerned at the constant disruption of the schooling of tens of thousands of children. An attempt to provide home learning kits for those in the first three grades was forbidden by the Israeli authorities. The school health services were also interrupted, likewise a third of the youth activity centres.

The UNRWA schools in the Gaza Strip were not so widely closed as those in the West Bank. But the schools were severely disturbed by strikes and curfews for up to 15 days a month. Tear gas was frequently fired into schools, some schools were entered by troops. An attempt to extend the school year for six weeks was refused by the civil administration.

7

UNRWA: AN INSTRUMENT OF PEACE

In all the pressing dangers and uncertainties of the Middle East, one international organisation stands out: the extremely capable United Nations Relief and Works Agency for Palestine Refugees in the Near East. The Agency has the ability to make a major contribution towards the resolution of the Arab-Israeli conflict: it has been working for Palestinian relief for over 40 years, meeting the needs which extend throughout Lebanon, the Arab Republic of Syria and Jordan as well as the West Bank and Gaza Strip. The work has called for wide resources of tenacity and professional devotion.

Since mid-1950 the Agency has provided education, health and welfare services to the needy among the 2.335 million Palestinian refugees registered with UNRWA. There are also a third of a million displaced persons from the 1967 War, who went mostly to Jordan and Syria. Although not the responsibility of UNRWA, they form part of the overall situation and an important element of the wider Palestinian problem.

The dual mandate given to UNRWA in December 1949 was to provide relief based on need and to conduct relief measures to promote the economic rehabilitation of the refugees. As a result, the Agency embarked on a complex relationship with the three Arab host governments and the Israeli military government of occupation in the West Bank and Gaza: the complexity arose because UNRWA had to function within the four very different territorial jurisdictions providing services which form a large part of the normal responsibilities of a territorial government.[1] This sharing of functions is difficult. It is yet more difficult when an occupying power exercises territorial responsibility for law and order and other functions of government, while a separate UN administration (inevitably suspected of bias towards the community under occupation) provides education and services to refugees in the refugee camps as well as relief for the most deprived.

Despite this very difficult role for a non-territorial administration, UNRWA has pursued a flexible and effective policy towards the Palestinians up to the present time.

The Agency's priorities have changed over the years. In 1950-55 the emphasis was on large-scale refugee resettlement combined with relief, education and medical services. Imaginative schemes in the Jordan valley and in Egypt were prepared, using water extracted from the Jordan and Nile rivers for irrigation and large-scale refugee resettlement. These schemes were rejected by the Palestinians who insisted that their acceptance would extinguish their rights of repatriation to their original homes. In the years between 1955 and 1959 UNRWA turned to smaller, self-help projects, still combined with basic relief and social services. Finally, in 1959, the Agency concentrated on education services expanded to include vocational training for refugee youth. These were designed to develop the latent abilities of the new generations 'to make them self-reliant, self-respecting and productive'.[2] Medical services have been maintained at a high

---

[1] Edward H. Buehrig: *The UN and the Palestinian Refugees: A Study in Non-Territorial Administration* (Indiana University Press, 1981) p 67.

[2] UNRWA, Experience and Works Project and Self-Support Programmes: An Historical Summary (1950-1962). Information Paper No 5. UNRWA, Beirut, September 1962, p 1.

level and relief continued as far as funds have allowed.

The result has been the creation of a modern educational system which is, at the least, equal to the best in the Arab world, and outstanding in the development of education for girls.

Over most of the last three decades, the UNRWA finances have been the cause of continual anxiety. The Agency has always depended upon voluntary contributions from 75 or more of the member states of the United Nations. Year by year these have been insufficient. Deficits have threatened UNRWA's very existence. Frequently the Agency has had to calculate its estimated date of collapse, so that funds would be available for redundancy payments to staff. On 30 June 1983, the Agency had received only 38% of the income pledged for the year. It had been on the verge of a cash crisis several times earlier in the year, most critically in April 1983, when the month's payroll was not covered until the last moment.

In September 1983 it became impossible to meet the cost of the general distribution of food to eligible refugees, except for those in Lebanon who were affected by the emergency and about 150,000 refugees elsewhere who were in extreme poverty, mainly resulting from the loss of the family wage-earners.

After the most stringent economies, the cash budget[3] for education, health, and relief services in 1985 was $165M. Against this, the prospective income was $138M. Reductions were made by stopping recruitment; increasing school classes to a teacher/pupil ratio of 1 to 50; cuts in budgets for transport, travel and educational supplies; cuts in building maintenance; cuts in new clinics and schools. These further economies involved serious risks such as the more intensive use of school buildings close to

---

[3] Besides the cash budget, there are food contributions, in kind, mainly from the USA, the EC and certain member states of the UN.

the point of collapse and keeping motor transport in service well beyond safe limits. The prospect of an enduring settlement to the Arab-Israeli conflict depends upon a new international determination to ensure the continuation of this extremely important work.

The war in Lebanon caused the Agency to set up a separate budget for emergency relief, supported by separate appeals to governments and international agencies. Planned expenditure was $53M. From the start of the Israeli invasion in June 1982 and until early 1984 emergency aid was given to 178,000 refugees. This amounted to 26,500 tons of food and essentials such as blankets and cooking stoves. Free daily meals were given to children under 15. UNRWA and UNICEF combined to provide safe water supplies to refugees 'many of them homeless and living in appalling conditions'; this was so effectively done that there was no epidemic. Mobile health teams took over from damaged and ruined clinics and other installations; schools were rapidly repaired; refugees were helped to repair damaged homes.[4] The killing of hundreds of civilians in the Sabra and Chatila districts by military action had grave implications for all Palestinians in Lebanon. Ten of the Palestinian staff were killed, many others displaced and rendered homeless; 90 UNRWA staff were detained among the 5,000 held by the Israeli army; three quarters of these were Palestinians. Forty-five staff members were arrested by the Lebanese authorities, of these 16 were still held, without charge, for long periods.[5] The Commissioner-General exercised the only procedure at his disposal, namely to report, to warn and to make

---

[4] UNRWA Press Release, HW/1985, 11 January 1985.

[5] Report of the Commissioner General of UNRWA for Palestinian Refugees in the Near East, 1 July 1982 to 30 June 1983. General Assembly Official Records: 38th Session, Supplement No 13 (A/38/13), New York, 1983, p 50, X-XIV.

representations to the occupying power. This was done frequently.

The Agency continued its special relief work in Lebanon until March 1984 when funds were exhausted.

During the remainder of UNRWA's present mandate it will become more and more important that its financial support must be secured by firm three-year pledges of adequate and timely support. This is to be no more than a formal recognition of the excellence of UNRWA's services and the vital need to maintain them through the years immediately ahead.

THE UNRWA EDUCATION, HEALTH AND RELIEF SERVICES

Education

The UNRWA 1988/89 Annual Report shows the steady rise in school populations since 1950. This explains the growing proportion of Agency finances committed to education. In spite of the very real difficulties, the achievements in education have been spectacular. Education is seized upon by the children and parents alike as providing the opportunity to overcome their present disadvantages. This urge for educational progress continues in spite of shortages of equipment and often inadequate school buildings. Many of the 628 schools[6] are old and dilapidated; three quarters of them have to provide for two separate schools and two complete teaching staffs, working in half-day shifts - an exceedingly onerous arrangement for both the school staffs and the children. Unfortunately, funds are only available for new

---

[6] Total of schools taken from the 1988/89 Annual Report.

109

school buildings to prevent *treble* shifting and to replace classrooms in danger of collapse. Nevertheless, results are excellent, and important advances have been made in pioneering the general education of Arab girls, who now very nearly equal the boys in numbers. All of the children display the most engaging keenness despite the overcrowding, sometimes sitting four at a desk.

Over 60% of UNRWA funds is now spent on this work. Inflation and a continuing increase in numbers lead to steady increase in costs.

Encouraging signs are the eight new schools recently built in Jordan with funds from Canada. Six more schools are being built there, two of them with help from the Canadian government and one by a wealthy Palestinian. The Canadian government has also helped to improve facilities in the Gaza Strip. Palestinian self-help has also done much to improve facilities in all refugee areas. But more than 450 new schools would be needed to end double shifting. School libraries are being started in 32 schools, but 125 more are needed; multi-use rooms are being found for new activities; vocational education is being started for young children at the elementary level, including gardening, electrical work, arts and crafts; girls are entering previously male spheres of education, such as mechanical drawing; secretarial courses are being supplemented by higher level studies in marketing and general management; electronics instruction is being kept abreast of world standards. All of this innovation has taken place despite local tensions and the state of unrest, particularly in the West Bank and Gaza.

UNRWA does not provide senior secondary education. This is the responsibility of host governments, but the Agency helps pupils who cannot get into government schools by giving grants to help them enter private schools.

There are just under 5,000 student places in the excellent UNRWA vocational and teacher training centres. Vocational training in the West Bank has been closed down for extended periods owing to the disturbances. The Agency provides 453 scholarships to universities.[7]

Health Care

There were 5.5M visits to UNRWA health and dental centres in 1988-89. Throughout the whole area of UNRWA activities there are 98 health units (and further mobile teams during the Lebanon emergency). Nine maternity centres are available and the Agency has arrangements for the use of 882 beds: nearly 41,000 people were admitted to hospital during 1987/88.

The whole approach to health care is progressive. Immunisation programmes in schools are becoming more comprehensive and there are hopes of complete coverage reasonably soon.

New health problems are appearing among Palestinians of early middle-age. Refugee children who were quite young in 1950 are now adults of 40 and there is evidence of arthritis, diabetes and blood pressure among them; these may be an aspect of the rising expectation of life from 40 to 60 years. More attention is to be given to the vulnerable groups; infant mortality may be reduced further by the help of WHO in starting in-service training

---

[7] Report of the Commissioner General of UNRWA, 1 July 1987 to 30 June 1988. General Assembly Official Records, 43rd Session, Supplement No 13, New York, 1988 (with figures added from subsequent two Annual Reports).

INCIDENCE TRENDS OF SELECTED
COMMUNICABLE DISEASES
(Rate per 100,000 eligible population)

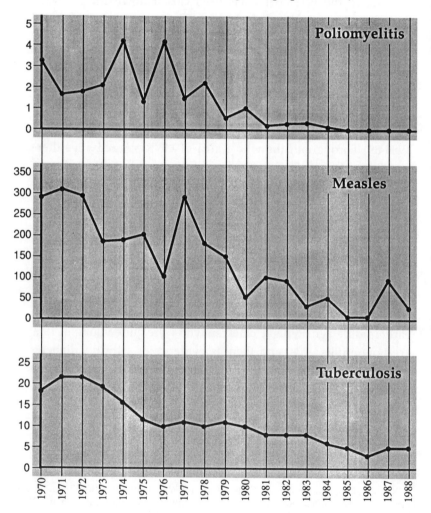

INFANT MORTALITY RATES
West Bank Camp Population 1975-1986

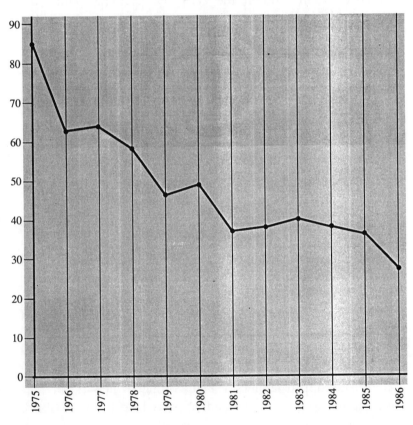

of UNRWA staff in child care. The pioneering work in rehydration has led to the adoption of UNRWA's methods worldwide. Improvements are being made in child feeding; on the spot laboratory service is being started in treatment centres, saving time and money. Dental care in schools is being improved and dental hygienists are being trained to relieve dentists of routine work; in addition, the Vocational Training Centres are now providing trained staff to support doctors in the clinics. The arrangements for supplementary feeding for the most needy refugee children are being improved by providing small dining rooms on the spot; diets are being improved and fresh fruit provided.

Relief

The suspension of the general basic ration programme for refugees (except for those in Lebanon) was forced on the Agency in September 1983. The issue of food rations is now confined to cases of special hardship: the 90,000 destitute widows and orphans; the aged; the physically and mentally handicapped and the chronically sick. Much of this destitution has been caused by the loss of family breadwinners.

Small cash grants and food are provided; bundles of used clothing are issued; sewing instruction is being given to adults. Brush-making is taught to the blind in Gaza; enough brushes are made to meet the entire needs of UNRWA, and the proceeds have made handicapped families self-supporting. A new project has been started to give mental and physical help to the disabled, using an old kindergarten building and voluntary instruction. There have already been encouraging improvements in children's health and a very good community response.

All of this has been achieved against a background of five destructive wars which have shattered countless families and whole communities. The wars and the violence have affected most of the 40 years of UNRWA's existence: scarcely a year has been free of threats, civil disorder and the endless task of rebuilding damaged refugee shelters. No single year of the refugee camps passed without fear. The tensions of the occupation are now high, and increasing.

In his 1987-88 annual report to the General Assembly of the United Nations, the Commissioner-General of UNRWA drew attention to the very difficult conditions under which refugees in the West Bank and Gaza Strip were living, especially those in the Gaza Strip. He stressed the growing bitterness and despair of the refugees over the lack of any sign of movement towards resolving their problems. His long and detailed account of relief and welfare work, in conditions of great difficulty, has clearly demonstrated the courage, tenacity and professional devotion of the Agency over the long years of conflict. There is good reason to hope that the existing Palestinian subordinate staff — under trained Palestinian direction — will play a full part in the achievement of peace between the Arabs and the Israelis and the evolution of the government of a new Palestine.

8

A STRUCTURE OF PEACE

At the start of this study, it was stressed that the greatest threat to world peace is in the Middle East tensions. Enduring peace still depends on the Palestinians achieving a homeland and a way of life which compares with that of any other people in the region. This has to be brought about in a manner fully acceptable to the Palestinians, to the Arab states, and to Israel.

Besides the Arab-Israeli antagonism there are deep divisions within Israeli society: between the two main political parties, Likud and Labour; and between the large number of small parties, each having special objectives, some religious, some secular. These small parties have had quite disproportionate political power, particularly when the two main parties are so nearly equal in strength. This is the case today.

In contrast to these difficult political circumstances, there are distinctly favourable practical developments on the ground. These provide real encouragement for progress in an eventual negotiation of peace. The most promising of them has been the constructive work of UNRWA over the last 40 years. The UNRWA educational, health and relief services have now moved far beyond meeting the day-to-day needs of the refugees, essential as this has been. They have achieved the stature of advanced professional services which would do credit to any government, however rich. Each of these services has a fine record of research and innovation which has brought very wide recognition. The total of UNRWA staff is now about 18,000, of whom only 120 were externally recruited. All the rest are Arabs, predominantly

Palestinian. The UNRWA *basic* organisation is suitable for continuing operation as part of a future Palestinian administration; the senior non-Palestinian staff will need to be progressively withdrawn, in a compassionate manner, with compensation, as was generally the case when British colonial territories became independent. On to this structure could be added the remaining needs of a complete Palestinian administration. This transition could be carried out with careful preparation and detailed discussion with the United Nations.[1]

The remaining essentials of a Palestinian government of the West Bank and Gaza Strip include justice, law and order, interior, external affairs, agriculture and animal husbandry services (already well established by the Israeli agricultural extension service); industry and trade; transport and communications. The experience of Palestinians in many Arab countries and in the West should make it possible to find qualified staff for the completion of a fully autonomous Palestinian government embracing the West Bank and Gaza Strip, with minor boundary adjustments and a strict minimum of Israeli settlements. This could bring a rapid change in the prospects of achieving a realistic peace.

There have for some time been two distinct levels in the relationship between Arabs and Israelis in the occupied territories: first the level of serious tension, developing since 1988 into violent antagonism between the Palestinians and the occupation forces. Secondly, in absolute contrast, there are the very favourable *underlying* Palestinian relations with the Israeli agricultural and social service staffs. In the course of many visits to the West Bank and Gaza Strip, the writer has witnessed the excellent relations between professional Israelis, agricultural, educational and

---

[1] This task will be closely similar to that undertaken by the Mandatory Government in 1920.

117

medical, and the Palestinians. This relationship has been consistently good and completely at variance with the relations between the security forces and the Palestinians. This wider more general relationship provides the best possible hope in the transitional years leading to complete Palestinian self-government.

The 1967 Six-Day War was a devastating experience for the Palestinians. Large numbers of them were driven out as refugees, mostly into Jordan. There was also a very serious loss of life and the loss of a great many homes. In spite of this background and the dispersal of so many refugees, by 1972 the Palestinians were cooperating fully with the Israeli agricultural staff and working hard to acquire new skills on the land. Relationships were distinctly good. The effects of the intifada will also be overcome by imaginative Palestinian resettlement. No intifada action has been reported against any Israeli agricultural, medical or other non-security staff.

Palestinian resettlement in the West Bank region would require the return of the greater part of the land and water resources appropriated for Israeli settlement and military purposes; also the introduction of pure water direct from the Yarmouk river. These measures, combined with the advanced systems of agricultural settlement, already well developed, should make possible extensive Palestinian resettlement on the West Bank.

It is difficult to overestimate the value of well planned and vigorous rural settlement in a situation of this kind. It could be dramatic in the development of improved Arab-Israeli relations. Modern agricultural methods (already widely adopted) could *double* the absorptive capacity of the land, contributing further to political stability. The possibilities of urban development must also be considered. If the existing refugee camps can be thinned out to reduce population pressures, to create open spaces and areas for minor industrial expansion, a start could be made on urbanisation, with proper services of all kinds. Certain of the camps in Jordan have developed in this way to an encouraging degree.

The cost of these developments should not be beyond the capacity of the major industrial countries of the West and the oil-rich Arab states of the Middle East, if both groups could join in financing an international recovery programme.

An important part of the peace negotiations must be the assessment of the scale and method of refugee settlement in the West Bank as the main reception area. If it were possible to revive the pre-1967 plan of the government of Jordan to bring the pure water from the Yarmouk river, under the increasingly saline river Jordan, for irrigation and settlement in the West Bank, it might be possible to resettle up to 250,000 Palestinians on the land, about half of them directly in agriculture. These measures could relieve the over-population in the refugee camps, enabling them to be converted into well planned urban centres with all normal municipal services. The detailed settlement and development plans would be drawn up in collaboration with the Palestinians themselves, particularly the balance between agriculture and the associated industries and other light industries.

The Gaza Strip is small; it is also overcrowded, as the original population is far outnumbered by the refugees. One possible solution to the resettlement problem might be to secure an extension of the Strip at its southern end. There is abundant groundwater, but desalination would almost certainly be necessary, and this is still costly in terms of agriculture.

An alternative and more attractive solution would be to negotiate with Israel to use, on a fully shared financial basis,[2] the

---

[2] Cooperation of this kind existed in the 1970's at the extraction point (Adasiye)

119

stormwater of the Nahal Besor (river) which crosses the Gaza Strip boundary five miles south west of Gaza town, on its way to the sea. This important water course is described in the Geography of Israel in the following terms:

> There is only one stream in the entire region, Nahal Besor, flowing down from the Negev Hills and sometimes carrying strong, dangerous floods. The sand spread over the region apparently causes the rainwater to seep into the gound quickly, and thus obviates the need for an extensive network of surface runoff. Nahal Besor, with its wide catchment area and devastating winter floods, has created a very large bed 100-150 metres wide, not only in the Beersheba Region, but also in the region of the Negev Coast. In the stream bed gullying has created a spectacular 'badland' topography; parts of the bed have been proclaimed a nature reserve. In the lower section of Nahal Besor, near the Gaza Strip border, construction of a large reservoir is planned to cover an area of about 4,000 acres. It is hoped that a considerable part of the floodwater (estimated at 20-30 million m^3 annually) will thus become available for farming.[3]

The potential of the Nahal Besor water course (which is a dry heavily eroded river bed much of the year) can be seen when it is in full spate after heavy rains near to its source forty miles south of Beersheba. The stormwater flow passes under a bridge on the Gaza Strip border road: it is then quite deep, fully 100 metres wide, and running very fast. It creates a strong impression of unjustifiable waste in an extremely arid region, where there is very great need for human settlement and food production.

The writer had the good fortune to see this remarkable flow of stormwater from the Negev, when it was in full spate. The water

---

where an agreed Jordanian share of the water is extracted from the Yarmouk river. It was planned to continue year by year.

[3] Efraim Orni and Elisha Efrat: *Geography of Israel*, (third revised edition, Israel Universities Press, Jerusalem, 1973) p 45.

was clear, and over a foot in depth.

There is no doubt that the Nahal Besor stormwater could be of the greatest value to the Palestinians and Israelis living in the region. At the worst, some treatment may be necessary, but this seems unlikely to be needed. A 4,000 acre reservoir shared by the two communities could transform agricultural production and, correctly handled on both sides, it could bring new hope of reconciliation in the Arab-Israeli conflict. With further experience, this water might assist in the wider development of the Gaza area in non-agricultural spheres.

There is a parallel development that should be of similar benefit to the people of the West Bank. This is in the upper reaches of the Yarmouk river where the construction of the projected major storage dam at Maqarin could be of great benefit to the region. Much preliminary development has been done on this extremely fine site high on the northern hills of Jordan, on the border of Syria. The potential capacity of this dam is 400 million cubic metres. The outline plan has long been clear on the ground. The time is approaching when these two exceptional projects could form a major part of an international plan to develop the full potential of these two areas.

Besides the very considerable task of Palestinian resettlement there are the two formidable problems of Jerusalem and security. Much valuable and discreet study has been given to the possibility of achieving a shared, but undivided, capital for both the Israelis and the Palestinians, in Jerusalem. This is encouraging, and could make a crucial contribution to solving the overall problem. At present, this would seem to be a matter for much later international negotiation, after substantial progress had been made in the territorial, resettlement and economic discussions.

Finally, there is the question of security of a future Palestinian administration. This would be greatly simplified if the new administration accepted demilitarisation except for the light weaponry needed for internal purposes of law and order. For a period of years, international or UN supervision would perhaps be necessary. The essential features of a demilitarised zone were outlined by Lord Noel-Baker in his Nobel Peace Prize study entitled 'The Arms Race'. This provides a suitable basis for the demilitarisation of the West Bank and Gaza Strip boundaries; also there should be progressive reduction, with compensation, of Israeli settlements to a strict minimum, possibly held on lease. The withdrawal of the Israeli security forces from the West Bank could then become possible, subject to acceptable international or UN guarantees. This would amount to the reversal of an important part of the act of occupation in 1967 and the subsequent appropriation of a large proportion of the territory occupied. Such a withdrawal under secure international arrangements, *including demilitarisation*, would lead to greatly improved Arab-Israeli relations. Under these conditions, the repatriation of Palestinian refugees could be worked out and resettlement started, following well established procedures. The creation of a modern rural economy in both regions would then follow. There have been indications that an arrangement of this kind would be acceptable to most Palestinians.

The State of Israel is now facing its most acute dilemma. Military success has left the country in control of the occupied territories but with more than two million Palestinians who bitterly resent, and now violently reject, the present situation. The options for Israel appear to be: (i) to absorb the Palestinians and their land, which would lead to a Jewish minority in an enlarged Israel early in the next century; (ii) to drive out the Palestinians into Jordan as advocated by some extremists, which would cause unimaginable distress and probably destroy Israel itself; (iii) to achieve a negotiated territorial compromise which would allow the Palestinians self-government in the West Bank and Gaza Strip, reduced in area only by the strictest needs of Israeli security.

International tribute has been paid to the remarkable results of the Marshall Plan, which was largely instrumental in achieving the recovery of countries devastated in the Second World War. It would be timely and appropriate if a similar plan were prepared now to finance the recovery of all the peoples who have suffered as a result of the Arab-Israeli conflict. The great economic strength achieved by the Federal Republic of Germany was however not only the result of the Marshall Plan, but also derived from the agreement between France and West Germany to pool their resources of coal and steel in what has become the European Community. What coal and steel were for them, water and land may be for Israel and her neighbours.

An international Middle East plan could increase the possibility of stabilising Arab-Israeli relations, and this in time could lead to a well founded peace. The plan might later be extended to encourage scientific development in the Sinai and Negev deserts and the search for a fuller basic understanding of the structure, function and dynamics of these, and other arid regions, so that productive human settlement could be developed without threatening the high sensitivity of the desert ecosystem. This would follow the expert Israeli research done in the Negev, and similar work in various Arab countries.

A stable peace, with acceptable territorial compromises and continuing financial support over resettlement problems, could gradually develop into a new cooperative relationship between the Palestinians and Israelis in the place of long-standing tension and conflict. A relationship of this kind is a real possibility. The

Israelis and Palestinians demonstrated their ability to cooperate constructively, soon after the 1967 War. The outstanding work of the Israeli agricultural staff and trained Palestinians in improving agricultural methods on the West Bank was the stimulus for achieving a remarkable improvement in relations in many individual Palestinian farming areas. The rapidly improved rural economy of the West Bank did much to restore Arab-Israeli relations. As soon as peace negotiations can clarify the respective Israeli and Palestinian areas, it would be the responsibility of the Palestinian leadership to work with the United Nations to adapt the basic organisation left by UNRWA. It could then be an integral part of a Palestinian government, able to work towards a fully cooperative relationship with the government of Israel.

There are grounds for hope that, with time and assured financial support to both countries, these two very able peoples will gradually achieve a new mode of lasting cooperation and harmony. There is a growing possibility that this cooperation could evolve further into a genuine association of partnership.

Besides concentrating on the expanding Palestinian agricultural economy, the opportunity would soon arise for the further encouragement of small scale industry in the improved areas, both in the changing refugee camps and in the new Palestinian settlement areas. It is in this work that the great skill of the Israelis could assist in developing a new relationship with the Arab peoples. As happened in the West Bank in the 1970's, there could once again be a local spirit of mutual help between the Arabs and Israelis. This would lead towards a wider, stable, and enduring relationship between the two peoples.

*

Since completing this study there have been a number of significant developments in the region. In particular, the Gulf War has had a profound effect throughout the Middle East. An important result of the War is the extended role for the United Nations in the region, reducing the risk of further military conflict. Also there has been an encouraging response to the initiatives of the United States, resulting in the agreement of Jordan, Egypt, Syria and Saudi Arabia to take part in peace negotiations with Israel, and Israel's acceptance of this generally, subject to some reservations about representatives of the PLO.

The fall of the Government of Yitzak Shamir was followed by the election of a left-wing coalition led by Yitzak Rabin. Speaking in the Knesset shortly afterwards, Mr. Rabin said he intended to hasten self-rule for the Palestinians and to have early discussions with the leaders of Jordan, Syria and Lebanon with the hope of agreeing upon peace talks. He undertook also to travel to Amman, Damascus or Beirut, at short notice, in the service of peace.

This declaration by the new Prime Minister was in close accord with the wishes of many Israelis.

There are four main areas in which peaceful progress should be possible. Firstly, further development within the Occupied Territories, where increased water supplies should improve agriculture and food production. Secondly, there will be the need to develop improved distribution and marketing of produce. This could include the canning of fruit products such as citrus juices, guava, pineapple and mango fruits. There may also be possibilities of dairy and meat production where these are not already established. Thirdly, there may be the need to develop further the various rural industries started in past years, such as building and transport services, as well as the smaller home industries such as bakeries, tailors, laundries and hairdressers. All of these could be seen in the West Bank and Gaza Camps in past years. These advances will need to be supported, in Palestinian areas, by improvements in electricity and water supplies, road-building and drainage.

Finally, there are two large schemes calling for development finance: the first of these is the large Maqarin Dam, on the border between Jordan and Syria. This will be part of the Jordan Valley Authority which has done the preliminary designs and a great deal of the preparation on the ground. There are other national and territorial interests expecting to benefit from this water, besides the Jordan Valley Authority, notably Syria and Israel. Important decisions have to be reached, perhaps with UN guidance. Such an international agreement would greatly contribute to peace.

The second major scheme is the Nahal Besor stormwater course which carries periodic and extremely large flows of water, after heavy rainfall in the Negev.

Both these schemes were seen by the writer. The Crown Prince of Jordan made it possible for me to see the Maqarin Dam Site in great detail, as well as the developments of the Jordan Valley Authority, including irrigation and advanced forms of settlement.

The Nahal Besor stormwater could be of similar benefit to the population of the Gaza Strip. This water could be led into a 4000 acre reservoir on the border of the Strip and used to transform agricultural production. It is no exaggeration to claim that these two exceptional schemes could greatly strengthen the prospect of lasting peace throughout the Middle East.

To ensure the fullest possible advantage of such developments there will be the need for the international community to provide substantial financial support.

APPENDIX

UNRWA Headquarters
Office of the Commissioner-General

Department of Education	Department of Health	Department of Relief Services	Department of Legal Affairs	Department of Finance	Department of Personnel and Administration
School Education teaching Methods Division*	Preventive Medicine Division*	Relief Services Division		Contributions Office	Personnel Services Division
Teacher Higher Education Division*	Curative Medicine Division	Supply Division Technical Office		Budget Division	
Vocational Technical Education Division*	Nursing Division*	Public Information Division		Accounts Division	Personnel Policy Division Administrative Services Office
Placement Office*	Nutrition & Supplementary Feeding Division			Management Division	
	Environmental Health Division			Data Processing Division	
				Audit Division	

*Located in Amman. All other units and all
departments heads located at Vienna

Further changes were made in August 1987 to improve coordination between headquarters and the operating fields and to
improve planning.